Of Things Unloved and Ignored

Published by Mission Point Press
2554 Chandler Lake Rd.
Traverse City, MI 49686
(231) 421-9513
www.MissionPointPress.com

ISBN: 978-1-943995-44-8
Library of Congress Control Number: 2017914701
Printed in the United States of America.

OF THINGS
IGNORED
AND UNLOVED

A NATURALIST WALKS NORTHERN MICHIGAN
RICHARD FIDLER

MISSION POINT PRESS

CONTENTS

Dedicated to the teachers and staff at the University of Michigan Biological Station, especially remembering professors Ed Voss, Fred Test, Howard Crum, Arlan Edgar, and Rex Lowe. Also a special thank you to Dan Palmer, my advisor in all things pteridophyte. The flame of interest you all lit still burns.

INTRODUCTION

It is easy to love lilies, robins, and honeybees, but harder to love poison ivy, leeches, and spiders. Eagles inspire us with their nobility, while freshwater sponges gain no respect from anyone—even if they have heard about them in the first place. Wolves are social animals like ourselves, thereby attracting our interest, while the sight of winged ants, another social animal, only impels us to purchase insect repellant. This book is about things we are unaware of either because we are too busy looking at other things or because we avoid the things we despise. Here, I place them in the limelight, if for only a moment, because they deserve our attention and respect: They are fascinating.

As a child, I was drawn to living beings usually avoided by my friends. I fed garden spiders grasshoppers, watching them bite and wrap up their prey in silk. Upon cruelly opening a snake up with a jack knife, I was fascinated to see that it had swallowed no fewer than four frogs. I was bitten by leeches, that experience terrifying me long after as it was relived in dreams. As a five-year old, I remember walking along a road after a rain and glancing down to see a salamander in a mud puddle. Picking it up in the palm of my hand, I stared at its unblinking eyes in wonder before placing it down. Sometimes I wonder if something didn't pass between us in that split second we took each other in. For me it did: I came to feel an inexpressible curiosity and love for all those things that lay all around us, ignored by most people or else hated by them.

As I grew up, my interests spread to astronomy—I learned the constellations and looked at the moon and planets through a three-and-a-half inch reflector telescope. I started a rock collection. I took to buying flower bulbs—*Rubrum* and *Auratum* lilies were my favorites—and planted them in an ignored area close to my house. Once, with a friend, I constructed what we called a "Venusian Garden," a small space demarcated by a circumscribing line of pebbles, and populated with the most outrageous life forms that were at hand: lichens, mosses, and bird's nest fungi among others. At that time, it was not clearly understood Venus was a fiery hell under all those clouds. We thought it was a tropical jungle.

INTRODUCTION

My interests wandered away from the natural sciences for a short time as I became interested in learning Asian languages, Chinese and Japanese. That interlude lasted but a few years. Looking at prospects for employment, I came to understand there were very few positions available in teaching Asian languages at the college level. I had to recalibrate—as the GPS system in my car often tells me when I have made a wrong turn.

In search of a livelihood, I remembered my childhood and the things I loved the most: the plants and animals that even now entered my dreams. I remembered the salamander and the mud puddle. A pathway opened up: I would become a teacher, a teacher of science—and that is exactly what happened.

I took chemistry courses, physics courses, astronomy, and botany. My favorites were the ones that took me outside to wade in streams in search of clams, walk the bogs to discover sundews and pitcher plants, scour beaches in search of wind-eroded stones (ventifacts), and capture fish for study in an aquarium. After I got my Batchelor's degree, I went on to get a Master's in Biology with all of courses taken at the University of Michigan Biological Station, located at Pellston, Michigan.

As music students devote themselves to the study of piano in summer camps, so do students of biology study their field with the same enthusiasm. I took courses about local vertebrates and invertebrates, courses about mushrooms and aquatic flowering plants, courses about mosses and fish. In the seventies and early eighties, the *organism* was the focus of most study at the Biological Station—as opposed to a modern perspective that elevates ecological thinking and resource management over other approaches. Students were expected to know what was out there—the critters and the plants. What a remarkable congruence between my interests and my education! It was a joyful time.

Thirty-one years passed as I taught 7th grade life science to hundreds of students. My classes would collect insects and leaves, dredge underwater insects from a nearby stream, and dissect flowers and fruit. Later, when I taught high school biology, I did not abandon these activities: it was more fun to dissect plants than read about them. You don't learn about biology as a collection of abstract concepts about nature—you do biology hands-on.

My students would often show me interesting things: a freshwater jellyfish, a mushroom like a dinner plate, a jumping spider with blue mouthparts, a snake greener than new grass, an insect as big as a fork. We would learn about them together sometimes, or else I would tell them what I knew. Their enthusiasm buoyed me up even if their frenetic energy wore me down at times.

Upon retirement in 2003, I became interested in the history of the Grand Traverse area, eventually completing four books about that subject. Sometimes, my interest in science intersected with that in history. Three chapters in this book reflect that intersection: *The Bay Boils and Surges*; *The Great Meteor of 1879*; and *Flooding Along the Bay: Are We Due for Another Seiche?* At first glance, they seem out of character with the title of the book, since everyone pays attention to eruptions on the Bay, a flash of a giant meteor, and unpredicted flooding along the waterfront. Indeed we do pay attention to these things, but forget them soon enough. That is another way we dismiss things and events—if they are long passed, why care them now?

It is time for the reader to begin this exploration of things unseen and places unvisited. I hope these encounters with them will entertain just as they did with me—or if not that, at least dispel the fear that often accompanies learning about new, often strange things. It is truly a remarkable planet we inhabit, and we need to get to know *all* of its inhabitants, not just the ones that have become familiar to us.

Two final notes: These chapters originally appeared in the online magazine, *Grand Traverse Journal*, which may be accessed at *gtjournal.tadl.org*. If readers would like to view colored photographs of the topics explored here, they can visit that site, entering appropriate words in the "search" box, words like "lichens" or "leeches." The articles in the magazine also frequently refer to websites that might enrich the reader's experience.

I offer my profound thanks to those who helped bring this book to print: Amy Barritt, for her enthusiastic support as co-editor of the *Grand Traverse Journal*; Sheila Stafford, for her wise counsel concerning the illustrations; and Dan Palmer, the fern guru of Michigan (and the world), for his erudition, encouragement and sense of humor. Producing a book is hardly the effort of the author alone. It belongs to many people—some, no doubt, left out here. My thanks extend to them, too.

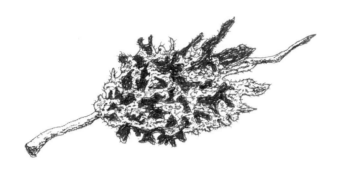

GODZILLA VS. SPONGILLA
A CONTRAST IN LIFE STYLES

A sponge is the antithesis of a super hero. It stays in place, sifting out plankton (microscopic algae and animals) from the water that passes through its body. Its body is not of great interest, lacking appendages altogether, not even possessing tentacles that might enwrap evildoers and others that would do it harm. Its personality is not engaging, either, since it does not have a brain.

To get its food, it has many small openings that take in its tiny prey, and a few larger ones that expel the water it has cleansed. The pumping system that carries on the circulation is primitive: cells with tiny whip-like appendages (flagella) line passageways, setting up the current. There are no robust hearts in sponges.

A simple animal reproduces simply. In some species of sponge, balls of cells (gemmules) form in mid- to late summer that can break off from the parent animal and grow into a new sponge somewhere else. This asexual form of reproduction is perhaps the most common means of making new sponges. However, sperms and eggs can be made inside its body, those fertilizing each other in a display that has nothing to do with affection. You wonder, without courtship, without males showing off what they've got, what is the point of reproduction like that?

Sponges do have a skeleton of sorts, however. In the ocean, some of them have a soft one made up of spongin, a substance that becomes flexible and absorbent upon being rehydrated. Those sponges have been used for hundreds of years in the Mediterranean Sea and elsewhere for scrubbing everything from floors to human bodies. Mostly replaced by plastic substitutes, they are occasionally used today.

Many years ago I took a course in invertebrates at the University of Michigan's Biological Station at Pellston, Michigan, and was surprised to learn that we have a freshwater sponge that inhabits our lakes: *Spongilla lacustris* (a few other species can be found here, too). As I observed it, its body most often was in the form of a greenish blob attached to sticks or pondweed–the green color, I found out, came from algae inhabiting the animal. It was not at all gooey or gelatinous, but felt rough to the touch and a bit like glassy bits stuck together when dried. Unlike its ocean brethren with their spongin, it had a skeleton made of crystal-like tiny elements made of silica, the same stuff that comprises most of our sand in Northern Michigan.

At least one animal appreciates Spongilla—but not for its appearance or life habits. Spongilla fly larvae feed on it with zest, later pupating to become small flies we are certain to ignore among the multitude of other flies that hatch in lakes and ponds. No life form—not even the sponge—is too humble to escape predators.

Spongilla is very particular about where it lives: it must have the cleanest, purest water around. For that reason, it is considered to be an indicator of pristine, unpolluted lakes. Far from being a pestilence, freshwater sponges are a gift. We should not condemn them for what they are not—gifted superheroes of the animal world. They are not delicious, not cute, not pretty, but they do constitute a component of our most treasured biological communities, the clear lakes that grace our landscape in Northern Michigan. Let us rejoice in their presence here.

THE MILK SNAKE
AN ANIMAL THAT DOES NOT MILK COWS

Milk snakes do not milk cows, contrary to legend. They do hang around barns and other structures–sometimes houses. Someone I know shares her dwelling with occasional milk snake intruders which apparently enjoy living in the crevices of the foundation. It does little good to let her know that they are only looking for rodents and other small varmints—she does not like them. To her credit, they have become only an occasional nuisance, and are only evicted from the premises rather than summarily decapitated, a common response of humans.

I saw one quite recently, three feet of torpid elegance stretched across a bike path near where I live. Fearing for its life—since it

THE MILK SNAKE

nearly blocked the right-of-way of bicycles—I stamped on the ground to get its attention. With apparent nonchalance, it moved to one side and then into the tall grasses beside the river, its tongue flicking out every few seconds as snakes do.

Indeed, why do they do that? Reference books tell me that this is their sense of smell, but that statement is not quite accurate, since the actual organ of smell is inside their mouths. The tongue only samples the air outside. Since they don't bring air directly past their olfactory membranes, then they can only smell whatever comes to them on the wind, a strange mechanism at least from our point of view, since we can sniff. What smells would they be sensitive to? Rodents, one might guess, and other milk snakes, females especially—if a male snake is the prime actor.

Milk snakes are harmless, but that does not mean they will not attempt to discourage those who would cause it irritation. Like many of its relatives, it will coil, hiss, and strike to incite fear in the hearts of its perceived enemies. It should be forgiven for that behavior, not beheaded.

These creatures are most commonly seen in spring and fall. They go after their prey after nightfall, seeking out mice with their flicking tongues, ready to wrap themselves around them in an instant, squeezing them so they cannot breathe. That is what constrictors do.

Milk snakes are given the name *Lampropeltis triangulum triangulum*, the "triangulum" element referring to a triangle or Y-shaped marking at the top of its head. In larger snakes dull red bands decorate its body, but smaller ones will have brighter red stripes bordered with black, all set upon a creamy white background.

After your initial surprise at seeing one, you will have to admire this animal for its stunning appearance. As so many snakes and reptiles are disappearing because of habitat disruption, they are to be treasured all the more. Let us live in peace with them.

THE MOST DREADED WILD PLANT
POISON IVY AND ITS RELATIVES

Poison ivy, poison sumac, poison oak: the three poisons we have to take care not to touch. The third doesn't grow here, so we don't need to worry about it. Somewhat rare in Northern Michigan, Poison sumac is a tall shrub that grows in wet places—I have seen it in the Platt River valley, locally. Ed Voss's magnificent floral guide *Michigan Flora* shows a cluster of counties with the species: Benzie, Grand Traverse, Leelanau, and Antrim. It is much more common downstate.

Poison sumac will not be confused with other sumacs, the staghorn sumac, for example. That plant has red berries and grows along fields and edges of hardwoods. As a teacher, I sometimes had to quell students' fears that they would break out from touching staghorn sumac. Unlike that familiar shrub, poison sumac grows in places where you get your feet wet. If it has berries at all, they are white. The leaves have the shiny look of poison ivy, but have 7-11 leaflets. Persons in search of pretty autumn color for their homes may be surprised to learn they brought it into the house.

Poison sumac (*Toxicodendron vernix*) is closely related to an Asian plant (*Toxicodendron vernicifluum*) which is used to make lacquer in Japan and elsewhere in Asia. While serving in Japan, a dermatologist friend told me that patients came to him with a rash similar to that of poison ivy on the backs of their thighs. The cause turned out to be toilet seats covered with the offending lacquer.

Poison ivy grows in a variety of plant communities: sand dunes, banks, shores, and along roadsides and railroad tracks. In the north, it does not climb trees, but remains as a small shrub, scarcely growing taller than two feet. Its shiny green leaves are, indeed, in threes ("leaves of three, let them be"), but that characteristic is not at all helpful since strawberry leaves come in threes, too. In contrast to the shrub form, it frequently takes on the growth habit of a vine in Southern Michigan, climbing a variety of trees, often to great height. Manistee County, according to Voss, is the farthest north this variety is to be found.

Are two such radically different varieties—one a shrub and the other a vine—really the same species? In most characteristics—leaf position and shape, length of leaf stems, inflorescence (arrangement of flowers on the stem), number of flowers, fruit size—they are similar, but not identical. The vine form has aerial rootlets to cling onto tree trunks, while the shrub form has none. If they are the same species, they should form intermediate forms upon crossing the two. Have they been crossed to see what the offspring look like?

Unfortunately, my source—William T. Gillis's article in the *Michigan Botanist*, Vol. 1, 1962—talks only about one failed attempt. An early frost killed the buds on the growing hybrids. Gillis did attempt to bring the northern rydbergii form to southern Michigan to see if they would begin to take on southern characteristics. They did not.

Let us leave the subject to say that poison ivy is a highly variable plant. One characteristic that all forms have is that they possess urushiol, the offending substance that causes the skin reaction in some persons. It is not volatile, so you cannot get the rash from merely standing close to plants: you must break the resin canals in the leaves in order to be exposed. Once exposed, it may take one or two days to react, or—in some cases—only a few hours, depending on the sensitivity of the person afflicted. Dogs and cats can carry the allergen on their fur, and smoke from burning leaves can cause serious trouble. It can even be carried on water—at least in the case of poison sumac, the species that loves to grow with roots in the water.

Not everyone is sensitive. Some persons can handle leaves and fruit with impunity. However, you cannot always count on previous insensitivity to avoid the rash since sensitivity can change over time, and in either direction. Steroidal creams and lotions ease the suffering of those afflicted, and the itching and angry blisters will disappear over time. Still, a person will not want to suffer this assault every year. So much the better to learn these plants and avoid them.

COMMON MERGANSERS AND THE ITCH

Swimmer's Itch plagues many Michigan lakes. Children are especially affected as itchy red bumps appear on legs and torso, soon after swimming. Little can be done to alleviate the itching—the old remedy of baking soda is probably as good as any. In a few days it disappears on its own, anyway.

The cause of the itch has been known for many years: a tiny parasite inhabits snails that shed them into the water on warm summer days. These *cercariae* are neither bacteria nor viruses, but a member of the flatworm phylum. In short, they are worms. Many years ago, at the University of Michigan Biological Station, I remember seeing them emerge from snails confined to a watch-glass under a low-power microscope. Compared to other such water creatures, they weren't that small. You could see them with your eyes if you cared to look.

After leaving the snails, apparently tired of the pace of life there, they swim around looking for a secondary host, frequently invading diving ducks such as the Common Merganser. Finding one, they bore through its skin, somehow finding one another in the circulatory system to mate (I believe the animals are bisexual). Afterwards, they migrate to the digestive tract where they produce eggs ready to be shed into the water with the duck's feces. Gaining the freedom of open water, they locate snails to infect, thereby completing the cycle.

We humans should be bystanders to this unwholesome series of events, but for one thing: the cercariae mistake us for ducks. Only after entering the outermost layer of skin do they realize their awful mistake, but it is too late for them: our body's immune system reacts to kill them off, that response leading to an angry, itching bump, swimmer's itch.

Various methods have been used to control the pest. At least two of them have been tried locally: copper sulfate and removing duck populations. Copper sulfate kills snails, one of the hosts, but that method has been largely abandoned because it is not particularly effective in the long run and because it has harmful effects on other life.

Getting rid of ducks is easier said than done. You can't shoot them all—after all, there are game laws and many of us (including me) like them. One technique is pyrotechnics. At first I thought this had to do with firecrackers and bombs to drive away flocks, but that is not exactly so. As applied to duck control, pyrotechnics has to do with firing a variety of noisemakers including propane cannons, thunderboom sticks, and bird bangers. A loud noise sends flocks flying, no matter what the source.

Glen Lake has tried this method for several years with inconclusive results. The Glen Lake Association on its website reports the itch still is bothersome, but not as bad as at Higgins Lake, where no such control has been attempted. For some persons, the intermittent detonations may prove as annoying as the itch.

A friend whose family owns a cottage at Glen Lake for many years tells me that the lake has always had a swimmer's itch problem. The red, itching bumps were a rite of summer. Usually, they do not discourage children to the point they will not go in the water. Swimming and splashing in the water are just too much fun.

There are some things you can do to avoid swimmer's itch (aside from scaring ducks and poisoning snails). There is some evidence that the cercariae are to be found more often on sunny, warm days, especially close to shore. Onshore winds drive them close to beaches where children are likely to play. Shorter swimming sessions might make infection less likely, too. Unfairly, suntan lotions often contain compounds that attract the itch organisms. Parents cannot catch a break—they must protect their children from the sun and from annoying creatures in the water. Apparently you cannot do both at the same time.

My reaction is that we will probably have to use these common sense measures of control—at least for now. As a duck lover, I hate to see flocks constantly chased off lakes by loud noises. Besides, how long will it take for them to get used to booms and pops? After all, the sounds of traffic in New York City used to be so quiet that they were ignored in 1850. Now, in 2017, it is no different, only we accept 70-decibel noise as normal. Wouldn't the ducks do the same as we did—learn to ignore the noise?

WHY DO LEAVES CHANGE COLOR IN THE FALL?

"Why" questions in science often find ready answers. Why do we have night and day? The Earth turns on its axis. Why do we have seasons? The tilt of the Earth in its path around the sun. What makes the wind blow? Solar warming of the atmosphere. The physics and chemistry of a situation provides us with answers.

Sometimes "why" questions are more difficult. Why are oranges orange and apples red? Why do birds migrate? Why do leaves change color in the fall? Those questions do not depend directly on physics at all. Do they even have answers?

In the case of leaves changing color, there actually is an answer based on physics and chemistry. As the days shorten, plant hormones cause a layer to form in the leaf stem (an abscission layer) that cuts off water supply to the leaf. Leaf cells with chlorophyll die off, that green pigment rapidly degrading. What is left are more resilient pigments, the yellow carotenes and the red anthocyanins. Trees turn red and orange and yellow and, Presto! We have explained why leaves change color.

But another "why" question remains: of what advantage is it to the tree that leaves change color? Here evolutionary biologists wage pitched battles. Is color change somehow "adaptive?" That is, does it have something to do with the tree's survival and reproduction? Or is it just something that happens, unrelated to those things?

Though relatively ignorant about these matters, I tend to cling to the belief that some things "just happen." They have nothing to do with enhanced survival and reproduction of species. The question "why" is only an expression of our human intelligence, ever demanding explanations for phenomena that have none.

I could be wrong about it—and sometimes I wonder how anyone could ever prove conclusively certain traits are adaptive. Is that because my own nature causes me to lean one way or the other? Is that very quality adaptive? Understandably, those concerned with such questions are prone to headaches. I hope you are not so afflicted.

THE LAST PLANTS TO BLOOM

Which native plant is the last to bloom before the onset of winter? Everyone knows Chrysanthemums, but they aren't native to Northern Michigan. Certainly, goldenrod blooms late, as do asters. Mostly goldenrod has finished by the time our most elegant aster, the New England Aster (*Symphyotrichum novae-angliae*) begins to bloom.

It can be found growing in moist places in the sun, its hairy leaves clasping the stem giving away its identity even before the flowers appear. When they do open, they present a glorious purple, sometimes almost a deep red. They do bloom late, sometimes as late as mid-October, but they are not the last to flower.

Jerusalem artichokes (*Helianthus tuberosus*), a native sunflower, show their bright yellow flowers at about the same time as New England Asters. Standing as tall as seven feet, they prefer open fields, forming dense thickets of flowers as they spread from underground rhizomes—which make a fine food if the preparer has enough time and energy to clean and cook them. Jerusalem artichokes grow tall, but will not be confused with the more common sunflower used for seeds enjoyed by humans and birds alike. Jerusalem artichokes, (sometimes called 'sunchokes', brighten our lives at a time the days grow shorter and shorter, but they aren't the last to bloom.

The last to bloom is witchhazel (*Hamamelis virginiana*), a small tree that grows at the edge of the forest or as an understory tree. Its leaves are distinctive with wavy margins, never toothed as most leaves are. Its flowers become most apparent just after its leaves have turned yellow and fallen off. Four thin yellow petals can be seen hanging from twigs sometimes as late as November. They aren't as spectacular as the New England aster or the Jerusalem artichoke, but they give us joy that a plant has the fortitude—or foolishness?—to brave days of 45 degrees at a time when pollinators are all dead or sleeping.

Witchhazel not only cheers us up at the end days of autumn, but it presents itself as a useful and interesting plant–useful, because its extract gives us an important astringent used in folk medicine, a treatment useful wherever swelling is a problem—and interesting because it can explosively shoot out its seeds from their capsules. Earlier in autumn they do just that. At such times it might be a good idea to wear safety glasses when walking in a grove of witchhazel because seed missiles can fly 30 feet in the air, certainly with enough force to put out an eye! (I hope readers know me well enough to suspect foolery).

Let us take joy in the last flowers of autumn. It will be many months before the crocuses send up their bold stalks in March.

FRESHWATER JELLYFISH
CUTE, AND THEY DON'T STING

Students frequently confront teachers of biology with a variety of organisms: snakes captured under porches, wild birds rescued and nurtured at home, preying mantises temporarily housed in glass jars, pet hamsters brought to school in their wire cages, and—occasionally—creatures one doesn't see regularly. That was the case when a boy lugged a large bucket of water into the classroom one September day. His question was the kind I welcome the most: *What are these?*

I looked inside the bucket, at first not seeing a thing as I focused on the bottom of the bucket. Then I saw them, swimming in the water column, tens of white, almost transparent disks, each one the size of a penny, swimming—is that too strong a word?—keeping themselves from sinking to the bottom. Astounded because I had never seen them before, I croaked out, "Do you know what you've found? Freshwater jellyfish! They're rare...where did you get them?" The boy, proud of his accomplishment, replied, "High Lake!" High Lake! High Lake had freshwater jellyfish! I wondered if I should report this finding to the University of Michigan.

Since that time much has been learned about freshwater jellyfish. The source I had used concerning these organisms, Pennak's *Freshwater Invertebrates of the United States (1953)* was outdated even at the time my classroom adventure occurred. The book emphasized how rare the animals were, having been found at only fifty locations throughout the country. As I read about them today I get a different impression about their origin, frequency and distribution across the lower 48 states.

The fluttering disks I saw in the bucket represented the medusa stage of the jellyfish, the sexual stage in the life cycle, the stage that produces eggs and sperms. However, the creature usually prefers the ease of asexual reproduction—a statement supported by the observation that all of the medusae in a lake might be male or else female, never a mixture of the two genders.

Students of Greek mythology might remember the word "medusa", a monster with a hideous female face surrounded by venomous snakes, its visage so terrible that humans would be turned to stone upon beholding it. The jellyfish medusa, thankfully, does not possess that power. It is named after the many tentacles that hang from its margin, a reminder of the monster's snakes. Indeed, like the snakes, it does possess venom—in tiny darts called "nematocysts"—but these are not robust enough to penetrate our skin. They cannot "sting" us like their relatives, the Portuguese Man of War.

How does the jellyfish reproduce without sex? It spends much of its life under water in the form of a polyp, a tiny but not microscopic form without tentacles that pinches off the little caps that become the medusa. Sometimes it does not even bother with that, simply budding off a new polyp from its side. Boaters and swimmers may not even see medusae in the water for years at a time. The animal produces them when he/she is ready.

They are not native to North America, having gotten here from China most likely with shipments of tropical fish and aquarium plants. Fifteen years ago High Lake was one of the earliest lakes affected by that introduction. They are not rare: freshwater jellyfish are found in bodies of water in almost all of the states east of the Mississippi River as well as many more out west. Outside of the United States they are now found in North and South America, Australia, and New Zealand, almost always in temperate locations. Alas, my excitement at finding rare fauna has cooled considerably.

Another invasive species! I anxiously turned to Wikipedia to read about its effects on local ecosystems: What foul deeds is it performing on our freshwater lakes? At present it is not clear what harm they are doing. They do not seem to disrupt the major feeding relationships among the animals we care about, the fish, birds, and mammals. Certainly they feed upon near-microscopic members of the zooplankton—the animals that feed small fish—

and occasionally upon minnows themselves, but their presence seems benign—at least so far.

That bucket of water from High Lake did open my eyes to something I did not know existed, even if it proved not to be the rarity I had imagined. It made me aware of another living form I had never heard of. Does stimulating my curiosity add to the value of an organism? If so, I have come to value the freshwater jellyfish.

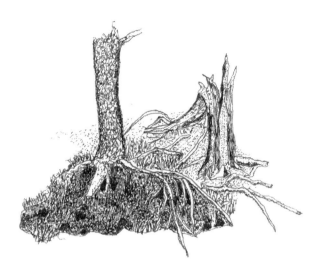

BEYOND TIPPED AND SHATTERED TREES
HOW WIND STORMS AFFECT FORESTS

Anyone living in Northwest Lower Michigan within a region extending from Leelanau through Kalkaska counties, will not forget the big storm of August 2, 2015. It was one of those signature events that cause you to remember exactly where you were when it happened. I was on the phone with a friend: we talked nervously, wondering when the connection would go dead, all the while thinking we should both head for our separate closets in case the roofs of our homes should blow away. Trees bent the way you see them do in videos of hurricanes and trash containers became missiles driven by the wind. In fact, on the basis of observed damage, the wind speed did exceed that of a category 2 hurricane in places, more than 100 miles per hour.

BEYOND TIPPED AND SHATTERED TREES

What do storms like that do to forests? Are there winners and losers in such a catastrophe? What effects can be observed after one, fifty, and a hundred years later? These are the questions that intrigued me as I walked through a devastated forest in Leelanau County, a few weeks after the Big Blow-down.

Mostly, the trees tipped, though a few were broken off at the middle. Earthen mounds containing tree roots made walking difficult as you took circuitous routes to get to places that used to be reached directly. The uneven ground of mature forests is due to tipped trees, some brought down a century or more ago. That is one long-term consequence of the storm: the hills and valleys of the new forest could remain for centuries.

A hardwoods in Michigan is generally covered with last year's un-decomposed leaves from last two or three years. Called leaf litter, it acts as a blanket, keeping moisture in and repelling the growth of small wildflowers, ferns, and other small plants. When the leaf litter is torn apart as it is when a tree tips over, opportunities abound for seeds waiting for their chance. They sprout and grow rapidly, their growth speeded by sunlight that touches the forest floor as tree canopies no longer provide shade. Along with natives, invasive plants like garlic mustard thrive in the disturbed ground. It is a changed habitat for all and those best adapted take advantage of their genetic heritage.

Certain trees win out in the competition for sunlight, casting others in shade as they overtop them. Shade intolerant trees grow the fastest—birch, black cherry, poplar red pine—while shade tolerant trees like sugar maple, American beech, and white pine bide their time in their shade. Before long, only the seedlings of those trees will dominate the forest floor, since only they can tolerate summers' complete shade. Poplars and black cherry (together with scattered oaks and maples) will dominate the first generation of trees on the hilly moraines of Leelanau and Grand Traverse counties. In time, they will be replaced by hemlock, beech, and a more dense population of sugar and red maples.

Naturally, a few middle-sized trees will survive a massive blow-down after a storm. After wind storm, with sunlight flooding in as the dense overhead canopy disappears, they respond to the changed conditions for growth. Buds under the bark spring to life, sending out small, leafy branches. Called epicormic sprouting, this phenomenon has serious consequences for those wishing perfect timber for logging, since the wood grain is interrupted by new vascular tissue that supplies the new branch. Look for epicormic sprouting in forests damaged by the August 2nd storm.

Secondary effects of a severe windstorm are too numerous to count. The loss of nests and dens that occupied old trees, the loss of stable food sources like acorns and beechnuts, the disappearance of animals that prefer the cool, deep shade of a mature forest (like land snails), and the opening of hilly terrain to erosion are four obvious ones, but even those only scratch the surface. Of course, the winners will move in—the deer that browse on shoots of poplar, ground squirrels, rabbits, blackberries and raspberries, and uncountable weed species—as the older residents die or move out. It is a scene that has been re-enacted for untold thousands of years.

Whenever something catastrophic happens in nature, we know it is wrong to take sides—since some living things require the housecleaning that enables them to thrive. At the same time, we cannot help but grieve for what has been lost. After all, isn't a mature hardwoods rarer and more precious than acreage covered by poplar sprouts? Virgin timber is very hard to find in Northern Michigan: Ever since the nineteenth century loggers have destroyed those ecosystems without mercy. So it is that we feel a pang in our hearts when the big trees go down and the sunlight pours in. We know we have lost something that took centuries to form. The Big Blow-down damaged far more than human property. It destroyed a natural relic that is not easily replaced.

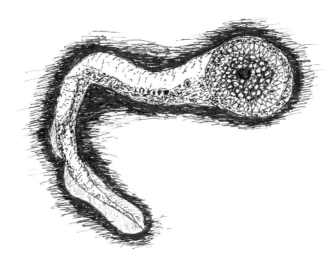

A KISS OF DEATH
THE LIFE OF THE SEA LAMPREY

There are few animals in the world that get less respect than lampreys. They are ugly, lacking fins and the grace of a recognizable face. They are slimy. They are deemed inedible, at least in the United States. They parasitize fish we like to eat. They are the animals we love to hate, and yet…

My encounters with lampreys have been few, but always interesting. There was the time my fish class went to a lamprey weir many years ago, and allowed them to suck onto the palms of students' hands. Lacking jaws, that is all they could do—give us an intense rubbery kiss. Perhaps it was the time of year or else the disgusting nature of mammal skin, but they did not try to bore into our flesh to suck our blood as they might do with the Lake

Trout. It was hard to detach, its body not offering traction for the other hand to pull it off (scraping turned out to be the best method).

Earlier that day we had gone upstream with a box sieve, a wooden frame with a wire screen affixed to the bottom, to capture immature lampreys. We would plunge it into a muddy bank and swish it around in the water to wash out the mud and silt. What was left were—among other invertebrates—many several-inch long young lampreys. Many, if not most, were native to Michigan, not having invaded by way of the St. Lawrence Seaway as the parasitic sea lamprey did.

Our native lampreys seem content to wallow in the mud, straining out organisms from the water with gill filaments. They transform into adults, mate, lay eggs, and die, much as salmon do. The sea lamprey goes one step farther, leaving its stream for the Great Lakes, feeding off fish such as Lake Trout for one year or more, finally returning to a stream to lay eggs and die.

Because lampreys return to streams to spawn and die, they can be controlled by several methods. The simplest of these is to erect a dam to keep them from migrating upstream where they may find gravel beds for spawning and muddy banks for nurturing the young larvae. The Union Street dam on the Boardman river serves this purpose in Traverse City. Unlike the other bridges upstream, it will not be removed, in part, because of this useful function.

Another method of controlling sea lampreys is to poison them periodically with poisons that work only on lampreys. It is necessary to use these chemicals once every several years because the larvae spend so much time buried on mud, feeding on microscopic organisms.

Oddly, we humans are related to these creatures. While lacking a jaw and a skeleton made of bone, lampreys have a nerve cord running along its back, a larval rod-like structure in its back that evolved into a backbone, and gill slits towards the mouth. We all have those features as embryos, but they change into other things as we develop. Our gill slits morph into a jaw and the structures in our necks, and our dorsal nerve cord lies within a bony column of vertebrae.

Lampreys and their kin are the ancestors of the dominant groups that we know today: the bony fish, amphibians, birds, reptiles, and mammals. They are evolutionary throwbacks, relics of a time that preceded the appearance of more modern vertebrates.

The kiss of a lamprey is singularly unrewarding, both for that animal and for us. To an appropriate fish it is the kiss of death, since many fish die as their blood is drained out. It is a kiss of death: Is that the reason we cannot love these animals—they plague our sleep with night terrors? Are we remembering our ancestral past when, as fish, we felt the sucking disk attach to our side, the creepy sensation that spelled our doom? Should we let down our fears as the Europeans have done to feast upon these animals? I don't know—you go first.

However, should any readers be inspired to extend their range of culinary skill, I offer this recipe for lampreys taken from the 15th century, *A Noble Boke of Cokery*:

> *To mak a freshe lamprey bake To bak a freche lampry tak and put a quyk lampry in a pot put ther to a porcyon of red wyne then stop the pot close that he lep not out and when he is dyinge tak him out and put hym in skaldinge water then tak hym in your handes with alyn clothe and a handfull of hay in the tother hand and strik hym so that the skyn go away and saue him hole then weshe hym and cut hym out whart a straw brod from the naville so that the stringe be lowse, then slitt hym a litill at the throt and tak out the string and kep the blode in a vesselle and it be a female thrust in your hand from the naville upwards so that the spawn com out ther as ye tak out*

It was taken from the Middle Ages, so cooking methods will seem a bit unorthodox. However, the success of the preparation may explain why King Henry I of England died from eating a surfeit of lampreys. He could not hold himself back from eating them all.

AT PLAY WITH THE WATER BEARS

There are some animals that astound us by their oddity: the "duck-billed" platypus because it lays eggs, the sea horse because the male broods the young, the ant lion because it digs pits that entrap ants. Tardigrades beat them all, different in so many respects scientists scarcely know where to fit them in on the evolutionary family tree. They are like aliens, come from another galaxy far away.

Sometimes called water bears, they lumber about on eight clawed legs, looking ungainly and a bit loveable with their antics. Possessing odd mouthparts with sharp stylets that pierce the plants upon which they feed, they suck out cell contents as if with a straw. Did I mention that they love mosses and lichens—and that they require a microscope to be seen?

AT PLAY WITH THE WATER BEARS

I have encountered them twice in my career. First, long ago, I took a course in mosses. Upon immersing those organisms in water to rehydrate them, tardigrades associated with them spring back to life, too: like instant coffee, you just add water to get the thing you want (in this case, a living being).

The other time I saw them was at the beach when I would dig holes near the water's edge and watch them fill up with water. Upon examining that water under the microscope, I discovered enormous numbers of water bears. My research tells me that, in addition to mosses, they eat algae and one-cell creatures, too. If they can be found among the grains of sand at a beach, no doubt they can be found in many other unsuspected places all around us.

Besides being cute, tardigrades are known for their resilience. They can be dehydrated and pop back to life after years in dormancy; they can be frozen to absolute zero, the temperature of outer space, and resume their normal lives without an iota of stress or worry; they can be boiled, scarcely feeling the heat. In short, they appear to be super-animals.

If you wish to see water bears, do what I did: rinse a clump of moss with water, allow the washing water to settle and then use a medicine dropper to suck up some debris. Surely, through your microscope you will see the creatures lumbering about in search of food or a mate. If you do not wish to take the trouble to corral your own animals, you may visit a tardigrade website to study them second-hand through the usual search engines available to us all.

HOW HIGH THE MOON?

When a former science teacher can't sleep, questions come unbidden to occupy his consciousness. So it was one cloudy night when I conceived the following question: Does the full moon make a high arc across the sky during winter or a low one? After some consideration, I proposed an answer: at the solstice (December 20 or thereabouts), the full moon should mount high in the sky before it begins to set. Conversely, it should have a low trajectory in summer, never getting very high at all.

Such a question is hardly of the complexity Albert Einstein entertained when he came up with the General Theory of Relativity, but then—I am not Einstein. Little questions are fun to explore as well as big ones, and if you don't achieve fame, at least you gain a small glow of joy when you get something right.

HOW HIGH THE MOON?

My reasoning went like this. All the planets, the sun, and the moon travel on a pathway across the sky called the ecliptic, which travels through all the constellations of the Zodiac. Why they all do this is well known: they all formed from matter that formed a disc around the sun. While some are more out of kilter than others, basically they race around on the same racetrack, moving from constellation to constellation over the course of the year.

The sun at winter's solstice is in Sagittarius, a constellation that—in Traverse City, at least—is viewed low in the south in summer. That is why it doesn't get very high in the sky (and why the weather is so cold) in winter. When the moon is full, it is 180 degrees away from the sun—and must be in the constellation directly opposite Sagittarius, the constellation of Gemini. So... when the winter moon is full, it must rise high in the sky, at winter solstice higher than at any other time.

Comforted with that solution, I went to sleep, the agitations of my brain somewhat quieted. I would only have to wait for the next clear night around the full moon to see if I was right. I expected to see the moon at midnight, high up in the sky, as high as the sun gets at mid-day in June.

And that is what I saw. There it was, its brightness blotting out Gemini (though I confess, I did not want to get out of bed, get out my binoculars, and go outside to check out the stars on this cold night). My hypothesis was tested and was proved right! Such triumphs are the things that illuminate my life.

Now I must wait for the full moon in June, which, according to my theory, should hug the horizon, often getting lost in the branches of trees and behind hills all around. You will help me check that out, won't you? After all, June is just four months away, and you won't have to sacrifice yourself to the elements: Just bring a blanket and a bottle of your favorite beverage to enjoy the moon hanging low in the sky.

Of course, you can watch the moon ride high even in March—if you are content to look at the first-quarter moon. It will be in Gemini, just as the full moon was at the winter solstice. Check it out—but first, while you are trying to sleep, hunker down and visualize why that must be so. That is what I do.

A FORGOTTEN VOICE
THE WIND IN THE TREES

A landscape presents a view of the land, a seascape, a view of the sea. A soundscape shows us the panorama of sound around us: the roar of engines, the cheers of a crowd, the ever-present music that attends our presence in stores, the luff of wind in a sail. We cannot avoid soundscapes; silence is one, too, and the most important, since it frames the rest.

I will not talk of silence, but of the soundscape of the forest, the sound of wind in the trees. That sound, tuned out by most of us as we rush about attending to our duties, does not present a single soundscape, but a variety of them. The sound of the wind through white pines is one, and its pitch changes with its speed. Then there is chatter of trembling aspen, not just trembling, but leaves striking each other forcefully, percussion without end.

The scraping of oak leaves left in winter gives a sound picture of a February day, a memory of the warmer days of autumn. A gale through bare branches rocks the trees as it fills the air with a sound we are at loss to describe. Trees are musical instruments of the wind.

Thoreau had an affinity for the wind through the pines:

The white pines in the horizon, either single trees or whole wood, are particularly interesting. The wind is making passes over them, magnetizing and electrifying them... This is the brightening and awakening of the pines... As if in this wind-storm of March a certain electricity was passing from heaven to earth through the pines and calling them to life. ~ Journal of Henry David Thoreau, 1855-1861

In her childhood diary, Opal Whitely speaks of the whisperings of leaves in the wind:

Now are coming the days of brown leaves. They fall from the trees. They flutter on the ground. When the brown leaves flutter, they are saying little things. They talk with the wind. I hear them tell of their borning days when they did come into the world as leaves. And they whisper of the hoods they wore then. I saw them. I use to count them on the way to school. Today they were talking of the time before their borning days of this spring time.

A FORGOTTEN VOICE

They talked on and on, and I did listen on to what they were telling the wind and the earth in their whisperings. They told how they were a part of earth and air before their tree-borning days. And how they were going back. In gray days of winter they go back to the earth again. But they do not die. ~The Story of Opal: The Journal of an Understanding Heart (p.56)

There is a word that describes the sound of wind in the leaves: psithurism (pronounced: SITH-ur-iz-m). It is obsolete, but I would like to do what I can to bring it back to life. For the most part, words that describe things people used to experience in nature have been replaced by those that point to technology: smart-phone, email, wi-fi, blue-ray, and all the rest. Would it be too much to wake people up to psithurism, a word that refers to something we all hear regularly?

Research is unclear as to whether excessive noise causes mental anguish, but here the wrong question has been asked. Better than asking if noise has harmful effects on our bodies and minds, is asking if quiet and psithurism can uplift us. For me, it does.

To be reminded of psithurism, you can always go to the internet and click on an appropriate link, but it is better to go outside on a windy day and just listen. Behind the sounds of traffic, the wail of sirens, the distant roar of aircraft, the barking of dogs, you will hear the rustling of leaves and the singing of pine needles. It is always there on windy days, yet we have learned to tune it out. Let us learn to listen.

LICHENS
BROKEN PIECE OF LIFE, WRETCHED BITS OF BEING

O broken life! O wretched bits of being,
Unrhythmic, patched, the even and the odd!
But Bradda still has lichens worth the seeing,
And thunder in her caves—thank God! Thank God!

— *Thomas Edward Brown, quoted* Lichens of North America

More than 24,000 souls are buried in Oakwood Cemetery on Eighth Street. Their monuments fill sixty acres all told, the earliest ones dating from the 1860s. They are made of limestone, granite, and even zinc, the last material only used for a few persons buried between 1885 and 1890. Draped urns, lambs, weeping willows, angels, passages of Scripture—even baby shoes—are carved on them, symbols of grief and the hope of life to come. Besides these human expressions of emotion are marks Nature herself bestows upon the stone as a reminder of continual change: lichens.

Lichens are informally called "moss" by most people, but are different from that organism. Mosses have leaves and stems, for one thing, and lichens do not. A moss is a single organism, every cell with moss DNA, while a lichen is like a chimera (an animal made up of two different kinds—like a centaur). Its body is made of a fungus which has captured a colored food-making element, an alga or a kind of bacteria. Often forming a crust or spreading as a leaf-like thallus over a stone monument, many of them are stunning, especially when examined under a ten-power lens.

We think of organisms only when they impact our lives and, in this regard, lichens are no different from other living things. What good are they? What harm do they do? What is their role in nature? These questions tug at us even as we admire their beauty.

We can't eat them, though a few cultures—like the Inuit—manage to extract scant nourishment in extreme habitats like the arctic.

They colonize our statues and monuments, their slender filaments penetrating even hard granite to a few millimeters and softer limestone to a depth of 16 millimeters (more than a half inch). Lichens are colonizers: they move onto unfriendly substrates like tree bark, barren soil, or rock, creating patches of organic matter which are taken over by more complex plants like mosses and ferns. They are pioneers.

Lichens are not friends to sextons of cemeteries. Degrading statuary and carvings, they make inscriptions hard to read, obscuring names and dates. Only the scattered zinc monuments are free of the problem, that surface providing scant toeholds for colonization. Inscriptions on the oldest stones are scarcely legible, so encrusted with green and orange lichen growth that observers vainly scratch them away to capture the names and dates of persons long forgotten.

Yet we should not despise lichens, for they charm us with their intricate structure. Under the lens, some of them present an array of disks aimed upward, not to catch something from above but to give something off: spores. Called apothecia, these miniature dishes produce millions of fungal spores which enter the streams of the wind. Upon landing in a fertile place, they send out tiny threads and wait for the landing of the right bacteria or algae, photosynthetic cells responsible for growth.

Slowly the colonies grow, and we should be glad, since lichens only thrive wherever the air is pure and clean. It is well known that tree trunks downwind from polluting industries are bare of lichens. When our tree trunks are bare of them in Northern Michigan, when gravestones stand without those round patches of sage green, orange, and yellow, then we will know that the air has gone bad. We should take joy in the lichens around us.

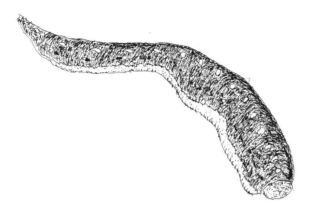

MEET *MACRODELLA DECORA*
A BLOOD-SUCKING LEECH

A naturalist must cope with whatever Nature deals out. Once when I took a course in invertebrates, I had to walk through shallow, warm ponds in the middle of summer, an action that would surely attract leeches (known by some as bloodsuckers). Sure enough, after traipsing through one particularly muddy body of water, I looked down to discover that one had attached to my leg. It was not only attached, but was apparently feeding: it wouldn't let go.

When one's life blood is being sucked out by a predator, one does not always behave rationally. Not entertaining the notion of spraying an offensive chemical on the animal so it would let go on its own, I used my fingernails to scrape it off. Not a good idea. The wound bled and bled, taking twenty minutes or so to stop. Thus, I learned about the anti-coagulant properties of leech saliva: leech bites don't readily stop bleeding because the creature injects hirudin, an chemical that prevents the blood from clotting.

The wound didn't hurt—I am told the clever leech employs an anesthetic as well as an anti-coagulant. It would never do to annoy a mammal to the point it would forcibly remove the animal feeding off it.: better to feed quietly and drop off to browse, sated with food and satisfied for any number of months to come.

This predator leech—the word "predator" is more appropriate than "parasite" since it feeds for only minutes instead of days and months—was *Macrobdella decora*, the American medicinal leech, the red-bellied leech. As its name implies, it sports an attractively decorated array of red spots, a possible design pattern for a necktie or a scarf. The animal is a distant relative of the earthworm with its concentric rings that encircle its body, marking off no fewer than 34 segments.

While the practice of leeching, using leeches to bleed patients, has fallen into disfavor since the nineteenth century, it still is occasionally employed in modern medicine whenever it is necessary to increase circulation to a blood-starved part of the body such as a newly reattached finger that has been accidently cut off, for example. I remember distinctly that in our own Munson hospital not too many years ago, a young girl had a finger reattached and submitted to treatment with leeches. "It's kissing my finger," she would tell visitors. Indeed, in a way, it was.

Most leeches do not feed upon mammals, preferring frogs, fish, and, especially, snapping turtles. Some do not attack large animals at all, being satisfied with earthworms and smaller creatures found in water. One of the largest leeches to be found in the area, its body extending a full six inches or more, seldom feeds on humans or their pets—the horse leech, *Haemopis marmorata*. I have observed this creature in Lime Lake, Leelanau County, where it can be seen rapidly scudding across the marly bottom, fully as capable of swimming as a fish.

Horse leeches sometimes are found on mud at the edge of the water. If they are grabbed to use for bait—as bass or walleye fishermen will occasionally do—they will readily try to climb out of the bucket, unlike other more docile species.

Leeches are given a bad rap. They seldom bite, they do not spread disease, they have medical uses, and they make good bait. However, the idea of having our blood sucked does not go down well with us. We despise things that do that—mosquitoes, black flies, or biting midges—and we cut them no slack. Perhaps, we should, though, with leeches. After all, they do us little harm—much less than mosquitoes—and at least one of them, *Macrobdella decora*, looks terrific!

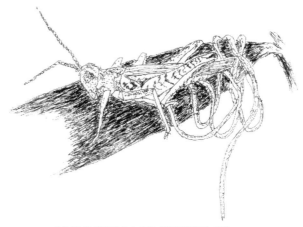

HORSEHAIR WORMS
A NIGHTMARE OF GRASSHOPPERS AND CRICKETS

In late summer in puddles, bird baths, pools, and even wet grass a long, thin writhing worm can sometimes be found, often coiling in extravagant knots, that behavior explaining one of its names, the gordian worm. As some readers may remember from school, Alexander the Great was confronted with the Gordian knot, having been told whoever untied it would rule the known world. After a few futile attempts he simply took out his sword and whacked it in two, presumably showing his contempt for that story.

Perhaps not as intricate as the real Gordian knot, the Gordian worm nevertheless displays a formidable tangle, its length sometimes stretching to 36 inches or more. It may be iridescent white if it has recently appeared, but rapidly turns a dark brown as time passes. For this reason—it takes on a more horsey hue—it is given another name, horsehair worm, perhaps in the mistaken belief that it originates from horses come to drink at watering troughs. In fact, it is associated not with horses at all, but with beetles, crickets, and grasshoppers.

Horsehair worms are common parasites of those insects. One summer long ago I participated in an informal survey of the grasshopper population to determine the rate of infection. Upon examination fully one grasshopper out of twenty harbored the tightly coiled worm, a death sentence for it as sure as the dissecting scissors that exposed its fellow traveler.

One question about the worm is unanswered: how do the parasites know when the insect is close to water? If it emerges in a dry hot place, it will surely shrivel in the sun. Somehow it must induce thirst in the grasshopper, driving it to approach water to drink. Does it control its host zombie-style, depriving it of its own grasshopper consciousness? Perhaps—and the image is strangely disturbing.

Upon emerging from its host the horsehair worm spends time in or near its body of water, eventually finding a relatively warm place to spend the winter. As waters warm in spring, the female worm sheds as many as 27 million eggs into the water, many of which are fertilized by the male as he passes over them. The young larvae creep along the bottom of their watery homes, seeking passage to the body of a cricket, grasshopper or beetle. The lucky ones hitch a ride in an aquatic insect, a larval cranefly, black fly, or dragonfly, perhaps. They form cysts within the those insects, wait for them to transform into adult winged forms, and ride out of the aquatic environment to a terrestrial one, a place where their host insects dwell. Leaving their "transportation host" after a rain or on a dewy morning, they wait for a hapless grasshopper or cricket passer-by. If good fortune allows them to be taken into the insect's body, they bore through the animal's gut and take up residence in the abdomen of its body, thereby completing its life cycle.

We should not hate horsehair worms. If they destroy one out of every twenty grasshoppers, surely they must save untold numbers of plants from being consumed by voracious insects. Even if their life cycle is not pretty, they provide a service for us. Even superficially repulsive wriggling worms have their place in Nature.

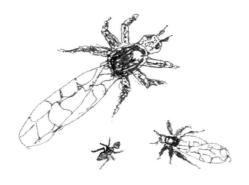

DON'T KILL 'EM, WATCH 'EM
THE NUPTIAL FLIGHTS OF ANTS

The voice on the other end was animated: "Come over now! They've got wings and they are swarming!"

I knew what she was talking about because I had discussed the subject previously. Ants were beginning their nuptial flights.

"I'll be right over! See what you can do to keep them from flying!" I answered with unrestrained emotion.

"A spoonful of sugar? A dead beetle carcass? I don't know what to do!" she wailed, enjoying the conversational gambit. I took no time to reply and jumped into the car with my camera.

My friend met me in her driveway when I arrived and led me to the scene. There they were: tens of small winged forms with two or three larger winged ones mingled among them. Some tiny workers, wingless bit players in the drama, milled around as if uncertain what to do.

My camera is not the best and my skills as a photographer are unremarkable, but I set it on macro, focused, and shot five times without a flash. The best ones became the basis for the drawing at the beginning of this chapter.

The word "nuptial" has to do with marriage, but that term has to be stretched to encompass the nuptial flights of ants. Males—the drones—finally emerge from the depths after having been taken care of the entire season long. No doubt some female humans can relate to that scenario. At the same time, a number of virgin queens were similarly readied for this day, the day they would be inseminated and fly off to found a new colony. It is a "marriage" in name only.

When the day length is right—late summer as a rule—and when conditions of humidity and sunlight somehow satisfy senses of the colony, the nuptial flight begins.

One-by-one the females depart, the males flying up with them. No doubt a chemical exuded by them induce the males to fly upwards, towards the light. However, the drones do not necessarily inseminate the colony's virgin queens: after all, that would be incest since all members of the colony have the same DNA. Under the best scenario, males from another colony would mate with them far away from the home colony.

The mating of ants takes place quickly and without ceremony. After separating, the "lucky" male flies away to die as his food reserves run out. He has served his purpose, and no longer receives the attention of his colony.

Meanwhile, the queen continues her flight, carrying the sperm in an internal packet which she will use over her entire reproductive life (several years to as many as 23). If she avoids interactions with predacious insects, birds, and car windshields, she will settle down and remove her wings through a deft motion of her body. Then she will seek to dig a burrow and lay her first eggs. It is the only "manual labor" she will have to perform because newly hatched workers will take over the mundane tasks of gathering food, carrying out the garbage, and taking care of new workers as well as the new princes and princesses of the next generation.

By the way, the new potential queens differ not at all from the workers: they only receive special food that grants them royalty. In a sense, it is like the transformation of a frog into a prince, since in each case a lowly, unprepossessing creature becomes something wonderful. Males, on the other hand, differ significantly from females: they have only one set of chromosomes (as opposed to two sets in the females). No doubt they, like human males with only one X chromosome, suffer certain genetic diseases more frequently than the females that surround them.

Winged ants cause psychological trauma in some persons. They grab insecticides and spray until the ground is littered with insect carcasses. I don't know if this account of ant reproduction will score any points with those who regard the only good insect as a dead insect, but I hope it might suggest that the winged forms are temporary and cause no harm. They do not eat our food, nor do they sting or bite.

It is not too late to see winged ants. In their book, *Journey to the Ants*, E.O. Wilson and Bert Holldobler describe the scene of a common ant that enacts nuptial flights during September:

> *The slaughter of failed reproductive hopefuls can be seen all over the eastern United States at the end of each summer, when the "Labor Day ant," Lasius neoniger, attempts colony reproduction. The species is one of the dominant insects of city sidewalks and lawns, open fields, golf courses, and country roadsides. The dumpy little brown workers build inconspicuous crater mounds, piles of excavated soil that encircle the entrance holes, causing the nests to look a bit like miniature volcanic calderas. Emerging from the nests, the workers forage over the ground, in among the grass tussocks, and up onto low grasses and shrubs in search of dead insects and nectar. For a few hours each year, however, this routine is abandoned and activity around the anthills changes drastically. In the last few days of August or the first two weeks of September—around Labor Day—at five o'clock on a sunny afternoon, if rain has recently fallen and if the air is still and warm and humid, vast swarms of virgin queens and males emerge from Lasius neoniger nests and fly upward. For an hour or two the air is filled*

with the winged ants, meeting and copulating while still aloft. Many end up splattered on windshields. Birds, dragonflies, robber flies, and other airborne predators also scythe through the airborne ranks. Some individuals stray far out over lakes, doomed to alight on water and drown. As twilight approaches the orgy ends, and the last of the survivors flutter to the ground. The queens scrape off their wings and search for a place to dig their earthen nest. Few will get far on this final journey...

Most winged forms die without our help. Insecticides are superfluous. Besides, why would anyone want to do away with a major natural spectacle?

NOT MOSSES, NOT ARMED
THE CLUB MOSSES OF NORTHERN MICHIGAN

Club mosses are not mosses, nor are they armed with clubs. They are small, however—only a few inches high on average—and are easily missed by hikers and those out for casual walks in the woods. Like mosses, they reproduce by spores, but, unlike them, they have vascular tissue to transport water from the roots (like flowering plants).

Most species of club mosses bear those spores on a stalk held above the plant proper, this structure called a strobilus (or, in plain English, a club). They shed their spores to the wind abundantly in the early summer: Just nudging a strobilus will send a cloud into the air, perhaps a danger to those with allergies, but perhaps not, since tree and grass pollen wreak far more damage.

Once in our history those spores had economic value. In the days before photographic flash, photographers would ignite a charge of club moss spores to produce a burst of light. Glass plate negatives were thereby exposed, making it unnecessary for subjects to spend many seconds in a strained pose. The spores contained tiny droplets of oil, which instantly caught on fire, much as flour dust ignites in grain elevator explosions.

Most club mosses are clonal: that is, they creep along the ground or else have underground rhizomes that put up new plants at regular intervals. An old clone can be many meters in diameter. In Leelanau county I have paced off one clone that occupied a circular space more than 30 feet across. There is at least one exception to the clonal habit of club mosses, however.

The shining club moss, *Huperzia lucidula*, grows in clumps, successive plants growing from horizontal stem often hidden under leaves on the forest floor. In addition to creeping forward in this manner, it spreads in a way that is singularly interesting to botanists and to people that like to play with other living beings. I count myself among the latter group, having spent many enjoyable hours turning click beetles over to watch them click upright with a bound, feeding ants to ant lions in their dens, and pestering pill bugs until they roll up in balls. The shining club moss offers as much amusement to me as those organisms do.

In August they have developed tiny springboards among the upper leaves, each one of which equipped with reproductive structures called gemmae, which are capable of growing into new plants. If you depress the springboard with the tip of a pencil, it will react convulsively, jumping upwards and releasing its gemmae.

How far do they travel? The answer is readily available to us. Look at the clump of *Huperzia* and see how far the farthest plant lies from the collection that comprises the clump. It grew from a gemma that was propelled from one of its parents, that plant often two or three feet away. Perhaps safety glasses are called for when the springboards are springing!

Huperzia is one of a few club mosses that does not bear its spores in clubs. In late summer you can see tiny yellow bodies in the axils of the leaves, each one a sporangium that will release its spores. The plant is unique in that way, and will not be confused with other lycopods (a word that refers to this group of plants). It is a joy to find one growing in a Northern Michigan hardwoods.

That is where I have always found them: a rich forest composed of beech, sugar maple, red maple, basswood, with an understory of ironwood and striped maple. It prefers a rich soil with a measure of clay. Some lycopods can be found growing on sterile soil in partial sun, too. Frequently the naturalist is surprised by their appearance in such unexpected habitats.

Club mosses have little practical value. By Michigan law they are protected from harvest by persons wishing to gather them on state land and sell them at Christmas time for decoration. Apparently, their evergreen branches remind people of cedar boughs at that bitter time of the year. Some species resemble tiny conifers and are planted in terrariums with varying success. Dried, they might pass for trees in a miniature railroad layout or diorama. In any case, they brighten our lives with their curious growth form and unlikely habits.

DANCE ALL NIGHT
THE MAGIC OF FAIRY RING MUSHROOMS

Fairy rings—circles of mushrooms growing in yards are known—and sometimes respected—by both children and grown-ups. "Respected" because, according to Irish and Welsh legend, they are places inhabited by the wee folk, fairies and leprechauns. Within the circles they dance, sometimes enticing a human passer-by to join them, much to his eventual regret. Once inside the ring, he cannot get out and is compelled to dance until exhaustion and death carry him away. Fairy rings deserve respect: it is at your own peril if you enter them.

Many kinds of mushrooms form fairy rings, but the commonest is probably *Marasmius oreades*, the fairy ring mushroom. It has an off-white cap with widely spaced gills, a slender fibrous stalk without a ring, and white spores. Unlike most mushrooms which decay and rot over time, *Marasmius* mummifies in summer heat, shrinking to a fraction of its fresh size, its firm flesh becoming tough and leathery over time.

If a fresh rain falls upon the mushroom, it perks up, expanding to its former size and regaining its firm texture. Not only does it appear to resurrect itself, it actually does that very thing. It has been shown that *Marasmius oreades* resumes its life processes, respiring and consuming food, even producing new spores on its gills. Somehow it goes into suspended animation for as long as a summer drought holds on, only to continue its business when growing conditions improve.

One hypothesis explaining the resurrection is the presence of a special sugar within the flesh of the mushroom, trehalose. After a dry spell, rainwater is absorbed, thereby dissolving the sugar—which enters cells, reviving and stimulating them to divide. This *Marasmius* is considered edible (but not especially delicious), having been incorporated into recipes for omelets, gravies, and even chocolate chip cookies. Perhaps the trehalose sugar helps the cookies taste better, though I suspect that the best change to the recipe would be to leave the mushrooms out.

Marasmius oreades grows in circles for a very good reason. It starts out when a mushroom spore lands in a favorable place for food, decayed matter underground. It spreads out a net of slender cells, hyphae (collectively called the mycelium), eventually reaching a size large enough to send up its first fruiting bodies, the familiar mushrooms we see above ground. Year by year the mycelium grows outward, forever producing new crops of mushrooms at its outer margin. The circle gets bigger, five feet in diameter, then ten, then even larger—certainly big enough to accommodate a large band of dancing fairies and an occasional hapless human.

Within the circle the grass may appear yellow and exhausted: the mushroom has absorbed nutrients in the soil, while at the edge it may be green and luxuriant as nutrients are released to be absorbed by the fungus and neighboring grass plants. Over-zealous yard managers sometimes try to get rid of the circles of mushrooms, preferring the monotony of turf to the disorderliness of fairy ring mushrooms. They are seldom successful.

To end this piece one can do no better than to quote a children's poem about fairy rings, this one unsigned:

If you see a fairy ring
 In a field of grass,
Very lightly step around,
Tiptoe as you pass;
Last night fairies frolicked there,
And they're sleeping somewhere near.
If you see a tiny fay
Lying fast asleep,
Shut your eyes and run away,
Do not stay or peep;
And be sure you never tell,
 Or you'll break the fairy spell.

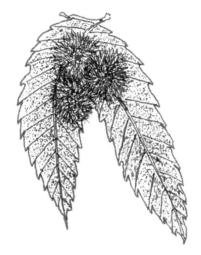

IN SEARCH OF THE AMERICAN CHESTNUT

In my spare time I read field guides—books that help me identify flowering plants, ferns, salamanders, fossils, and insects. It has always been so—going back to my grade school years—and I make no apologies for it. Such a hobby, while unpromising as a source of wealth or useful knowledge, has no downsides as far as I can see. And frequently it leads me onto pathways of delight, whenever a fringed gentian in a marsh comes to my attention, a fossil crinoid discovered upon the beach, or an ant lion pit dug along a sandy trail. Field guides make such delights possible.

So it was that I picked up Barnes and Wagner's *Michigan Trees* to spend a profitable quarter hour before bed. The page opened to the American Chestnut and there on page 208 the following passage appeared:

> *A plantation of chestnut trees, established in 1910 in Benzie Co., gave rise to a stand of several thousand offspring (Thompson, 1969).*

Checking the source (Thompson, 1969) at the back of the book, I discovered that an obscure Michigan journal, the *Michigan Academician*, published the original paper describing the plantation. Could I get a copy of it and find out if this mysterious grove of chestnuts still existed, disease-free?

Here it is necessary to provide background for my curiosity. The American chestnut, *Castanea dentata*, was a grand component of the eastern American hardwood forest throughout the nineteenth century. In Michigan it naturally penetrated as far north as St. Clair county and was locally abundant in Monroe and Wayne counties in Southeastern Michigan. Beginning about 1900 the tree suffered the attack of a vicious fungus, *Cryphonectria parasitica*, likely imported from Asia, which destroyed American chestnuts everywhere. By 1940 the tree had largely disappeared from American forests, though suckers from dead trees continued to sprout for years afterwards, only to die upon reaching maturity.

The American chestnut should be distinguished from the horsechestnut, *Aesculus hippocastanea*, a tree commonly planted around homes. That tree, a permanent resident arrived from Europe after white settlement here, displays candelabras of white blossoms in June, finally producing inedible nuts that resemble chestnuts in appearance. Contrary to expectation, it is not enjoyed by horses, neither the leaves nor the nuts, though folklore insists it cures COPD in those animals.

American chestnuts were planted in the Grand Traverse area from early times. I had seen individual trees planted near farms on Old Mission peninsula and had heard stories of trees planted elsewhere nearby. But had a whole grove of them survived, a grove planted in 1910? If they still lived, the trees would be more than a hundred years old. They would be magnificent.

The Grand Traverse Conservancy provided the key that would unlock the mystery of the hidden chestnut grove. In response to my query, Conservancy staffer Angie Lucas, plant expert extraordinaire, e-mailed me the *Michigan Academician* article. And there it was: the information I needed to find the chestnuts:

> *The grove, owned by James Rogers, is located at Chimney Corners (SE ¼ Sect. 35, T27N, R16W) at the top of the Point Betsie Moraine, a massive 300-foot glacial ridge which flanks the north shore of Crystal Lake.*

I live in Traverse City and am scarcely familiar with Crystal Lake, but I had a human resource that would guide me to the proper coordinates: Dan Palmer, resident of Leelanau county, knowledgeable in forestry, brought up in Frankfort, and familiar with the back trails of Benzie county. We would explore the north of Crystal Lake and find these trees hidden in Chimney Corners.

To those who know Benzie County, Chimney Corners is hardly obscure. It is a venerable resort with roots going back to the early twentieth century. The lodge stands now as it did in 1908, its stone fireplace dominating the space as you enter, grooved beadboard woodwork, electric lights from an earlier time, collections of beach reading from the fifties, and the grit of sand on hardwood floors. The proprietors kindly allowed us to walk the ridge to see the chestnuts: Just follow "chestnut trail," they said.

The three-hundred foot moraine was surmounted with breathlessness as our party proceeded up the trail. It was a steep climb through a maple, beech, and basswood forest of moderate age, but there was no sign of the sharply toothed leaves of *Castanea dentata*. Were we in the right place?

Then, up ahead, a clue, though not a felicitous one. An enormous white skeleton of a tree stripped of its bark with many of its larger branches fallen roundabout stood out in the shade of taller trees. It was long dead, likely a chestnut, given its size and location. My hopes dropped: They were gone, all of them.

Still, we kept walking and along the trail were more dead trees, but some of them had suckers at the base that brandished the green leaves of living chestnuts. The forest floor, though, was not littered with the burs that encased the shiny chestnuts. Reproduction was not happening here: the shoots would live for a decade and die before flowering. The chestnut grove was doomed.

As we walked out of the forest, there were more dead trees, but as we came into a sunnier place, the chestnut suckers—offshoots—were more robust, as much as five inches in diameter, some of them reaching twenty-five feet or more into the sky. Green spikes of flowers appeared at the end of twigs, vague promises that chestnuts might be found in autumn at this place. We found a few burs from last year, the chestnuts missing from inside, either because the trees had not enough energy to make the nuts or because squirrels had devoured them.

Cankers caused by *Cryphonectria parasitica* appeared on the small stems of the chestnut suckers: the trees were unhealthy and would not live much longer. It would be a race between their mortality and their ability to produce nuts that would grow into the next generation. Remembering the fate of the white giants within the forest, I would bet on the fungus to destroy the trees before they could reproduce. There is good reason that *Castanea dentata* disappeared from the eastern United States.

The story could end here, but there is another thread to follow. The Grand Traverse Conservancy has just acquired a beautiful parcel of land from the estate of Naomi Borwell. Located just inside Manistee county off Manistee County Line Road, it offers a diversity of habitats: hardwood forests, deep valleys, frontage on the Betsie River, swamps, and a developed farm planted with a variety of interesting trees: spruces, birches, hawthorns—even a row of shagbark hickories—unusual in this part of Michigan. Best of all, there is a grove of American chestnuts with diameters of twelve inches, standing 45 feet high—though the ugly cankers on the large branches indicate the disease has penetrated here, too. You get the feeling the chestnut plantation is waiting its doom—which lurks in its very near future.

In nature it is unfair to take sides, though we do it all the time. *Cryphonectria parasitica* depends upon American chestnuts for its survival, but the fungus does not charm us with its form or grace. I have read of numerous attempts to hybridize the American chestnut with Asian forms that have a degree of resistance to the disease: you can learn about those efforts at the American Chestnut Foundation, http://www.acf.org/FAQ.php It seems likely that blight-resistant chestnuts with American chestnut features will become available within a decade or two, though the degree of resistance has not been determined as of now.

Perhaps it will be years before we can obtain American chestnuts to plant beside our homes without fear of the fungus destroying the trees, but when that time comes, I will be among the first to get them, God willing. With its glorious history in our forests, its stately grace, its delicious fruit, the American chestnut is too splendid for us to abandon.

Postscript

Sometimes stories refuse to end, no matter how hard you try to bring them to a conclusion. A friend at the public library informed me that he was quite sure a Michigan champion American Chestnut could be found at the end of Old Mission Peninsula. After a few days he emailed me the specifics: according to the Michigan Botanist, Volume 37, 1995, an enormous tree could be found off Old Mission Road, quite close to the country store, a bit past a curve, off a drive heading towards a cherry orchard. Could it still exist 20 years later?

IN SEARCH OF THE AMERICAN CHESTNUT

How could anyone do anything but drive out there and find out? Surprisingly, the directions were easy to follow and, with the help of a neighbor, Jim Hilt, my friend Marlas Hanson and I soon observed a tree towering in front of us, an American Chestnut far larger than any we had seen heretofore. Its trunk was split into three stems, twisted each one of them, and the canopy spread above over a wide area. It showed a few dead limbs, but it was alive—and not in bad shape for an old tree. There was no evidence of chestnut blight.

However, there was something peculiar about the tree: one would expect American Chestnut saplings round about, planted by squirrels that forgot where they sequestered the nuts, perhaps. But there were none to be found—not one. A few old burs from the previous year were scattered around the base of the tree, the nuts gone. It looked as if the tree had bothered to produce the spiny burs, but either they were empty from the start or else contained nuts that were infertile—or maybe every single one had been consumed by wildlife. In any case this American Chestnut had no offspring

A Puzzle

Does the very character that makes the tree infertile cause it to be resistant to blight? In other words, this tree—and another located three farms away—are the only ones I have seen that have not succumbed to the disease. Do they avoid blight because they are incapable of reproducing? Or is the answer simpler—that the champion Michigan tree needs other chestnuts nearby in order to obtain pollen for fertilization and that its infertility has nothing to do with its resistance? I do not know the answer, but I would like to find out—but to investigate that thread would take another year or two or five, and this story must end sometime. And so, let us end it here for now.

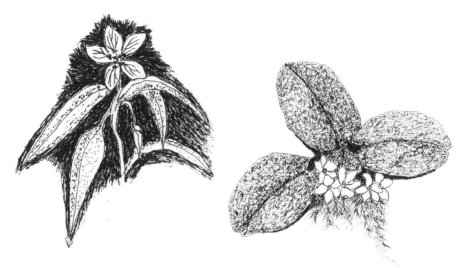

SPRING BEAUTY, TRAILING ARBUTUS, AND THE COMING OF SPRING

The first wildflowers of spring are Hepatica (Hepatica rotundifolia), Trailing Arbutus (Epigaea repens), and Spring Beauty (Claytonia virginiana). Most years, Hepatica is the first to show a white (sometimes lavender) blossom that occasionally overtops the previous year's maple and beech leaves on the forest floor. Growing nearby, Spring Beauty comes next, its white, candy-striped petals attracting a few bees and flies for pollination. Trailing Arbutus blooms in an altogether different habitat, a forest of pine trees and oaks. It often conceals its fragrant white blooms underneath its tough, evergreen leaves.

Hepatica is so interesting it deserves a full story by itself, so Spring Beauty and Trailing Arbutus will occupy us here. It is appropriate they are paired since they both figure in Native American legends about the return of spring. The following excerpt is taken from *The Red Indian Fairy Book*, published in 1917. Disregarding its somewhat racist title (Are Native Americans really "red"?), it tells the legend of the Spring Beauty, a story attributed to the Ojibwe (Chippewa).

Legend of the Spring Beauty
(Chippewa)

An old man was sitting in his lodge, by the side of
a frozen stream. It was the end of Winter, the air
was not so cold, and his fire was nearly out. He
was old and alone. His locks were white with
age, and he trembled in every joint. Day after
day passed, and he heard nothing but the sound
of the storm sweeping before it the new-fallen snow.

One day while his fire was dying, a handsome
young man entered the lodge. His cheeks were red,
his eyes sparkled. He walked with a quick, light step.
His forehead was bound with sweet-grass, and he
carried a bunch of fragrant flowers in his hand.

"Ah, my Son," said the old man, "I am happy to see you.
Come in. Tell me your adventures, and what strange
lands you have seen. I will tell you my wonderful

deeds, and what I can perform. You shall do the same, and we will amuse each other."

The old man then drew from a bag a curiously wrought pipe. He filled it with mild tobacco, and handed it to his guest. They each smoked from the pipe, and then began their stories.

"I am Peboan, the Spirit of Winter," said the old man. "I blow my breath, and the streams stand still. The water becomes stiff and hard as clear stone."

"I am Seegwun, the Spirit of Spring," answered the youth. " I breathe, and flowers spring up in the meadows and woods."

"I shake my locks," said the old man, "and the snow covers the land. The leaves fall from the trees, and my breath blows them away. The birds fly to the distant land, and the animals hide them selves from the cold."

"I shake my ringlets," said the young man, and the warm showers of soft rain fall upon the Earth. The flowers lift their heads from the ground, and the grass grows thick and green. My voice recalls the birds, and they come flying joyfully from the Southland. The warmth of my breath unbinds the streams, and they sing the songs of

Summer. Music fills the groves wherever I walk, and all Nature rejoices."

And while they were thus talking, a wonderful change took place. The Sun began to rise. Again the warmth stole over the place. Peboan, the Spirit of Winter, became silent. His head drooped, and the snow outside the lodge melted away. Seegwun, the Spirit of Spring, grew more radiant, and rose joyfully to his feet. The Robin and the Bluebird began to sing on the top of the lodge. The stream murmured past the door, and the fragrance of opening flowers came softly on the breeze.

The lodge faded away, and Peboan sank down and dissolved into tiny streams of water, that vanished under the brown leaves of the forest.

Thus the Spirit of Winter departed, and where he melted away the Indian children gathered the first blossoms, fragrant and delicately pink, the modest Spring Beauty.

(The same story, this time with a beautiful maiden rather than a youth, has been told about the Trailing Arbutus. It has been attributed both to both the Iroquois and the Ojibwe traditions.)

The final paragraph was added to the story by the narrator of the legend—or so it seems to me. For one thing, Spring Beauties have no fragrance, at least as far as I can tell. They are not pink, but white with pink stripes, and their blossoms last for only a day or two. Who would want to pick them?

However, the whole plant might have been harvested for another purpose: eating. Underneath the soil—sometimes as deep as six inches—a corm guards the life of the plant when it is not growing. Sometimes nearly as large as a walnut, it is prized as a spring food for all who love the woods. Without the bitterness of other leaves and roots, it can be roasted or eaten raw. Considering their beauty, it is hard for me to dig up very many of them, but at a time before forests were cut down, they would have provided tribes with a plentiful food supply in early spring.

Spring Beauties stay above ground for only a few weeks. Before the canopy of the hardwood trees fills in to block the sun, they complete their life cycle, bearing flowers and developing fruit before disappearing in early summer. For ten months they sleep in the soil, only sending up shoots after the snow has melted. Like Squirrel Corn and Dutchman's Breeches which grow in Northern Michigan hardwoods, it is described as an *ephemeral*, setting seed while the sun can still penetrate the leafy overstory. Their transitory nature makes them all the more dear to us.

Trailing Arbutus is an altogether different kind of plant. It's tough leathery leaves persist year-to-year, hiding the fragrant white flowers beneath. They live in the pine forest, appearing on mossy banks, though I have seen them in wet places like the Skegemog Preserve. Because of their beauty, their refreshing comment on the change of seasons, and the rich green of their leaves, they were commonly ripped from the ground for decoration. Here is an article lamenting the destruction of Trailing Arbutus from the *Traverse City Record-Eagle* dated 1923:

AGAIN PLEAD FOR ARBUTUS

Woman's Club Pleads for Vine
Great Patches of Bloom Are Rapidly Being Burned
By Thoughtless Persons

Some time ago, when it seemed that spring might be coming, the Woman's Club sent out a pleas to all seekers of wild flowers to use care in picking them so as not to disturb the roots.

Now that the Trailing Arbutus is in bloom this plea is again broadcasted.

To those who can remember back but a few years, the present feeble bloom of the spring's loveliest flower, is a most pathetic thing. In the plots which have been picked over year after year the vine is disappearing. Instead of a blossom which rivaled the apple blossom in size, the arbutus has shrunk to a tiny flower on a short stem.

A pair of scissors would prevent this gradual disappearance of this typically Michigan vine. It is the constant pulling up by the roots which has made barren the great patches of arbutus which not long ago filled the pine woods, so the Woman's Club urged all those seeking this spring flower to carry with them a small pair of scissors with which to clip the stems.

The article points out several things, both about the plant and about the times. It was formerly abundant and more prominent than now. From a blossom rivaling that of an apple blossom, it has "shrunk to a tiny flower on a short stem." Edward Voss, in *Michigan Flora*, states that the flowers are often nearly hidden beneath the leaves—scarcely visible to wildflower aficionados. To those who decry the stripping of stems along with flowers, he offers the consolation that that stem and flowers emerge from a "stout, woody tap-rooted crown", a hardy structure which may resist the savagery of collectors. Like the Spring Beauty (which is not related), the Trailing Arbutus seeds are distributed by ants which feast upon a food coat that surrounds the growing part of the seed.

I have never seen Trailing Arbutus with its stems held up high to display flowers as large as apple blossoms. Could it be that humans have gotten rid of that trait through genetic engineering? That is, by harvesting the largest blossoms did we drive evolution forward in the direction of smaller ones hidden under leaves? Clipped before they reproduce, the most showy flowers would not produce seed and would disappear over time–much as mowing has produced a variety of lawn weeds that complete their life cycles in dwarf form. It does not take DNA technology to change the gene make-up of organisms.

One more thing about the article: in 1923 the newspaper editor chose to publish an article warning about overharvesting a wildflower found in pine woods near the city of Traverse City. Would such an article be published today? I would argue, "No", since nobody knows about Trailing Arbutus. By "nobody" I do exaggerate, but only by a little. In earlier times the people of Northern Michigan were more in touch with nature: they paid attention to wildflowers and the creatures that inhabited the land around them. Now it is an unusual person that can identify Trailing Arbutus, let alone consider picking it to brighten up the house. Our obsession with technological gadgets—our iPads and iPhones–has replaced our connection to nature, that shift working to preserve wildflowers. Not all components of modernity serve to attack nature—thank Heaven.

Spring Beauty and Trailing Arbutus, two very different plants that announce spring in Northern Michigan, give us a sense of community, a belongingness that join us all in nature, time, and place. We welcome them, however different they are, because they speak of the end of cold and ice, the beginning of warmth and harvest. Let us go out and look for them in April, but only to admire them, not to pick.

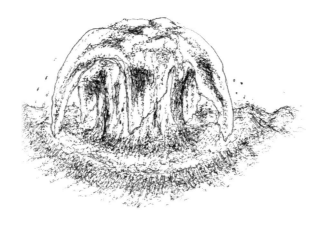

A STRANGE PHENOMENON
THE BAY BOILS AND SURGES

Like Sherlock Holmes, historians are on the prowl for interesting cases. At times they cry out with enthusiasm, "The game's afoot!" when they discover something that engages their attention so completely that it overrides their sense of public presence. So it was when I came upon the following article from the Morning Record, dated June 15, 1899:

> *The annual explosion in the bay, opposite the G.R. & I depot occurred Monday. The water boiled furiously for several minutes and finally burst into the air with considerable force raising a large body of water about four feet above the surface. These submarine disturbances have been a mystery for many years and as yet no expla-*

nation has been made to account for the disturbances.
The gushing of the water was observed by several persons
yesterday.

Lucille Zoulek's index to local newspapers indicated another article upon the same subject thirteen days later. It gave even more details:

Boiling Again

There was another submarine explosion on the bay
yesterday east of the G.R. & I depot. The water was
thrown into the air about 20 feet and the commotion
was vigorous and continued several minutes. Some per-
sons in a boat chanced to be over the spot at the time and
they had a lively time for a few minutes. This is the third
eruption of the kind this season.

The G.R. & I depot was located near the water where the Boardman River empties into the Bay. In the first account, the water boiled and burst four feet high, but in the second, it shot up some twenty feet high. Indeed, boat passengers nearby would have a lively time of it. This was not a trivial rise of the water which occurs as a result of different air pressures on the Lake basin, but was something far more dramatic.

Questions arise like the bubbles of the furious bay: Was the account true? Was it accurate? Had such eruptions been observed in the past—or afterwards? Did they occur at the same time of year? And, finally, what causes them? Most troubling to this historian is the bare fact that he is neither a geologist nor a student of the phenomena of the Great Lakes. Still, there is the love of seeking out answers, a curiosity that grabs you by the neck and pushes you forward. "The game is afoot!"

The first article indicated the phenomenon had been observed "for many years." The first thing to do would be to locate other articles that could give new locations, new times of year the eruptions occurred, and new descriptions that might shed light on its nature. A fellow historian searched not the deepest recesses of the state archives, but the deepest recesses of the internet. She turned up the following account recorded in the *Jackson Citizen-Patriot*, August, 1883:

> *In Grand Traverse bay recently, at some distance out in deep water, between Traverse City and Marion Island, the water began to boil and surge, and presently rose in vast jets to the height of from 10 to 20 feet. Being observed from the shore no details could be given on account of the distance, but the same thing had taken place years before and some two years ago, according to an account given by the Herald at that time, parties in a boat were so nearly on the spot that they were obliged to hasten out of its way. They describe the water as apparently boiling from the very bottom of the bay, which in that place was nearly or quite one hundred feet deep, bringing up with it vast quantities of mud and other substances and*

emitting an intensely unpleasant sulphurous smell. The area of the eruption, if it may be so called, was about twenty feet in diameter and the time about half an hour. At intervals the water would subside into calmness and then the commotion would begin again. It is said by old settlers that the same thing has occurred in other years. The disturbance is always in a line between Traverse City and the island. It is well known by old residents that there are places in the bay where salt water springs bubble up through the water, in the neighborhood of the island. It is possible there are submarine openings of other descriptions, either volcanic or otherwise. It is know to scientific men that there is a tract of country on the eastern shore of Michigan, in the neighborhood of Thunder bay directly across the state from Grand Traverse bay, where slight earthquakes are frequent, and in fact the bay was named by the Indians from the rumbling noise that from time to time was heard in the interior of the earth. It is possible that the tidal waves, as well as Traverse bay disturbances, may arise from volcanic action as a common cause, and all newspaper readers are well aware that there has never been a time within the memory of the present generation when the earth seemed to be in such a state of internal agitation as at the present, many of the known volcanoes of the world being in active eruption,

*now ones breaking out where none were known before,
and earthquake shocks, both slight and severe, frequent
in every part of the world.*

This eruption was in August! So they do not always occur in June. The location was somewhat different: Marion Island (now known as Power island) is some distance from the city. However, upsurges and boilings occur along a line that runs from Traverse City to the island. Would that imply an underwater seam of rock exists there? Could that suggest a cause?

This eruption occurred in a deep part of the Bay at a place "more than a hundred feet deep." Furthermore, it sent up mud to discolor that water and emitted a "sulphurous smell," an observation that set the editor to wondering if volcanic activity might be responsible. At a time before plate tectonics and fault lines were understood, that suggestion was reasonable: after all, weren't volcanoes like Vesuvius erupting all over the Earth? Krakatoa was making ominous rumblings, though it's eruption would occur later in August. In the light of our present knowledge about volcanoes and earthquakes we reject the likelihood of volcanic activity so close to home. There must be another explanation for event.

Once again, my historian friend comes to the rescue: she sends me a link to Alexander Winchell's, *A Report on the Geological and Industrial Resources of the Counties of Antrim, Grand Traverse, Benzie and Leelanaw in the Lower Peninsula of Michigan*, printed in 1866. On page 59 a clue jumps from the page that helps me to understand the cause of the "strange phenomenon" upon the bay.

The well authenticated existence of an ancient salt spring on the neck of land connecting Harbor (Hog) island (now, Marion or Power island) with the peninsula, I should regard as a confirmation of this opinion [that the salt/gypsum layer found in SE Michigan should be found elsewhere in the lower Peninsula] since, if a fissure existed in the overlapping rocks, the brine would tend to rise by hydrostatic pressure, as an artesian boring. Deacon Dame of Northport, one of the oldest residents of the region, has furnished me with detailed information which seems to fully authenticate the current tradition relative to the former existence of this spring.

Winchell is saying that a layer of salt water lies trapped between two layers of rock in a manner that reminds him of rock formations in southeastern Michigan. The liquid is under pressure and, if rock layers are exposed, it will come out to make a saltwater spring. I wonder: if a wider fissure in the overlying rocks occurred, wouldn't the brine jet out to form a fountain twenty feet high? Is the cause of boiling and surging due to the sudden release of pressure as an underwater seam of rock opens?

If only observers back then had tested the water for salt! Asking them to taste it would have been more than anyone should ask. I predict it would be salty, perhaps so salty nearby fish would have been killed. At any rate, the salt springs found locally could be linked to the eruptions in the bay.

A STRANGE PHENOMENON

The mystery of surging bay water has been ignored for most of the twentieth century because it was not observed over that period of time: I have been unable to find further descriptions of it after 1899. Why has the bay been so quiet over the past hundred years? I do not know, but I would like to find out. Are there geologists out there who would like to participate in this investigation? Goodness knows—there are tons of questions to be answered.

THE EARLIEST BUTTERFLY OF SPRING
THE MOURNING CLOAK

It is a sunny day in March, the temperature hitting close to sixty degrees and I am out hunting for Mourning Cloak butterflies. The drifts of snow still covering the north slopes and hollows do not discourage me because I know their habits: they emerge early in spring–earlier than any other butterfly–seeking sweetness in damaged trees leaking sap as well as mates to continue their life cycle. Up ahead among the hard-wood trunks of beech and maple I see a dark flutter—Mourning Cloaks, two of them flying in a tight spiral, a mating dance. I raise my hands to the sky for a moment as an expression of joy at my discovery. As I do, another Mourning Cloak I had missed in my concentration upon the first pair draws close and boldly lands upon the sleeve of my jacket. It flexes his wings once or twice and I beam with joy: What an intelligent and friendly animal this is! We bask in each other's company.

Mourning Cloaks overwinter as adults, crawling into warm spaces underneath bark or stones, close to soil that remains unfrozen all year long. Among the earliest wildflowers, the Spring Beauties and the Hepatica, they dance in the sunlight, ready to mate, lay eggs, and die, thereby completing their life cycle within a calendar year. The eggs, laid upon host plants poplar and willow, hatch into dark spiky caterpillars, creatures one would hardly guess would change into a splendid adult butterfly.

The adult is mostly a uniform purple-black, a muted yellow border on its wings with a row of blue dots inside of that. Having lived a year already, its wings might appear battered and faded, not furnished with the glowing colors it showed upon its emergence from its pupal case.

This butterfly, like many others, is territorial, males often proclaiming their rights by lighting on the highest object around, understory trees, for example, or hands outstretched in joy at having found Mourning Cloaks in the first days of spring. Or, then again, with that behavior they might be proving they are especially intelligent and friendly insects!

I have found Mourning Cloaks in Northern Michigan hardwoods—consisting of beech, sugar maple, white ash, black cherry—in the months of March, April, and May. They disappear for much of the summer as eggs hatch into caterpillars, caterpillars transform into butterflies, and butterflies "sleep" during the hottest summer months, *aestivation* the term given to this period of dormancy. In late summer and early fall they appear again, the new adults, seeking nectar and food to get them through our long, cold winters.

The Mourning Cloak is the animal equivalent of Spring Beauty, Trailing Arbutus, and Hepatica, the first wildflowers to appear in spring. We welcome it as we do those flowers, the earliest sign that warmth is returning to the world. Whether you visit the woods for morels or for wildflowers, keep an eye out for these butterflies. And if you hold your hands up, you just might get one to land on you.

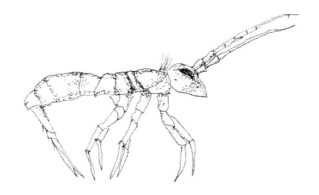

THE MICROSCOPIC WORLD OF
SPRINGTAILS AND SNOWFLEAS

"I love to watch the jumpers when I water my houseplants," she said.

"What jumpers?" I asked.

"Whenever I water them, you can see little bugs jump up. Want to see them?" She went to get her watering can. As she soaked the largest plant, a Norfolk Island Pine, I could see nearly microscopic beings jumping several inches from the soil.

"Do you see them?" she asked. "Aren't they cute?"

"I do see them—and, yes, they are cute. And I think I know what they are."

Some years ago, when I first began to study ecology, the class set up a Berlese funnel, a device designed to capture animals in the leaf litter, the topmost layer of the forest floor. It consisted of a large metallic funnel into which a sample of leaves, sticks, and soil had been placed. Above was an incandescent bulb, low wattage, which provided the heat required to bake the critters out. As the sample dried, they would migrate to the narrow part of the funnel, eventually falling into a jar of alcohol. The menagerie of tiny animals was too diverse to describe in detail here, but one inhabitant was both abundant and memorable: springtails.

Springtails are only a millimeter or so long, only visible to our eyes if we are paying careful attention. They have six legs and an odd lever at the end of their abdomens that springs forward, propelling them up in the air. In the past they were regarded as insects, but now, in the day of DNA analysis, they have been removed from that taxon. They are now classified in their own taxonomic group Entognatha, that name pointing to the animal's internal mouthparts.

Mostly springtails live on dead and decaying plant matter. They are partly responsible for converting the dead leaves of autumn into black humus. It takes hordes of them to accomplish that work: one estimate of their abundance suggests there might be at least 100,000 of them per square meter.

In winter, not all species of springtails are dormant. On warm days some of them—snowfleas as they are commonly called—can be seen hopping on the granular snow, sometimes discoloring it with their tiny bodies which measure less than a millimeter in many cases. They have small lever affairs on their abdomens that are under tension when locked in position. When aroused, they unlock the mechanism and spring upwards, sometimes 50 or 100 times their body length. One wonders how much fun that must be!

In the waning days of winter, look carefully at the snow at the base of trees. Can you see them hop when you move your hand close?

You can watch snowfleas without the sting of cold if you go online, of course. But if you want to remember the encounter, it is best to go outside on a blustery day in early March and try to find them, yourself: the shock of cold embeds them in your memory.

THE GREAT METEOR OF 1879
THE BIGGEST ONE TO HIT HERE IN RECENT TIMES?

Last year's meteor fall in Chelyabinsk, Russia had a counterpart in Leelanau County more than a hundred thirty-five years ago. The Grand Traverse Herald January 30, 1879 edition tells the story:

> *About half past 2 o'clock Tuesday morning, an enormous meteor passed over this region. The accounts given by the few who saw it are so conflicting that it is difficult to settle upon anything definite in regard to its direction or apparent size. We have had it coming from every point of the compass and straight up and down: it varied in size from a pint bowl to a hogshead; it struck in the bay and it struck all along the shore; it traveled "as fast as a*

horse could trot," and it "flew like lightning." We didn't see it ourselves. We were asleep, as all good editors should be at that time in the morning. Those who did see it were evidently too startled to observe it closely. What is known is that it was an immense ball of fire, and that the darkness was made light as noonday, and that a terrible explosion followed its appearance—or disappearance, no one seems to know which. The night watchman at Hannah, Lay & Co., says that he saw it explode and that it flew into minute pieces like star dust. (The one thing that all agree upon is the explosion. This was heard with equal clearness and with like effect at Mayfield, thirteen miles south of this place and at Williamsburg, twelve miles east. We have not heard from other directions. The effect was of an earthquake shock. The houses were shaken, windows shook and dishes rattled upon the shelves. A swaying motion seemed to be given to the buildings as an upheaval and settling back. If the meteor had not been seen it would have been thought an earthquake shock. It was a big thing any way and that fellow that was close by when it fell or exploded must have thought "something dropped.

A watchman, most likely the Hannah and Lay Company employee mentioned above, provided a more detailed description of the meteor's passage to the editor of the Herald, Thomas T.

Bates. Somehow, his notes turned up in the Report of the 49th Meeting of the British Association for the Advancement of Science (1879) in an article called *Report of Observations of Luminous Meteors.*

> *Was on watch, passing from due west to east; saw a great light; turned quickly, and saw a ball of fire over my right shoulder; turned to left and watched until it disappeared; when first seen it appeared about as high as ordinary rain-clouds; appeared to me larger than full moon; full moon looks to me to be 18 or 20 inches in diameter; meteor appeared to pass me, and move out of sight at about the rate of speed a descending rocket has after its explosion; had a good chance to see it plainly; just after passing me a singular thing occurred; a ring of fire seemed to peel off the meteor itself, and this followed the ball of fire out of sight, but dropped a little behind it; it was perfectly distinct, and appeared to be hollow, for I could see a dark centre. Everything was as light as day. I looked at my watch as it disappeared; it was just 28 minutes after 2 o'clock. I passed on my beat, and shortly the terrific explosion came. It shook and jarred everything around. I immediately looked at my watch, and it was 32 minutes after 2.*

From this account and others, Professor Kirkwood of the British Association for the Advancement of Science, commenting about the event, drew the following conclusions: The fireball first came in sight nearly 100 miles over a point about 30 miles S.W. of Traverse City and disappeared about 26 miles above a point about 42 miles N.E. by eastwards from that town. The whole visible track was 124 miles, and its projection on the earth's surface 66 miles in length from a direction S.W. by S. towards N.E. by N. Of the time of flight, which was described as several seconds, and of the real velocity, except that the observations indicate a rather slow motion, nothing definite can be affirmed. (The author goes on to speculate that the meteor may be related to the 'Cancrid' meteor systems which occur in the months of December, January, and February.)

In 1879 there were few inhabitants living in the Grand Traverse area, this fact explaining why, outside the *Herald*, little note was made of the meteor in other publications of the time. Surely, an event that lit up the night sky as "light as noonday" while producing an explosion loud enough to "shake houses" would have aroused the interest of larger populations living in Chicago or Detroit. Newspaper editors there would have written about it in order to answer questions of readers. However, there is no apparent mention of the meteor in the Detroit Free-Press or the Chicago newspapers.

A more precise word than "meteor" for this event is "fireball". Nowadays that term refers to a very bright meteor of magnitude -4 or better, brighter than the planet Venus. They are relatively common, the Earth receiving several thousand a day, most over oceans, mountains, deserts and other inhabited regions. Very few reach a size large enough for a fragment to impact Earth and even fewer that light up the sky as if at midday, producing an explosive thunderclap.

Another term used to describe fireballs is "bolide", the word connoting an extremely bright fireball, one that explodes, often leaving fragments on the surface of the Earth. Even bigger than a bolide is a "superbolide", a meteor with a brightness more than -17 (the sun has a magnitude of -26). If the 1879 account describing the meteor as brighter than the noonday sun is not an exaggeration, the Traverse area certainly encountered a superbolide.

The *Grand Traverse Herald* was not through describing the meteor. After penning the above article, editor Bates later talked to R. S. Bassett, a local fisherman, who offered a first-hand account. Bates continues:

> *We have just seen Mr. R. S. Bassett, who has a fishing shanty within a few rods of Fouch's dock at the head of Carp Lake, seven miles northwest of this place. Mr. Bassett was awake and saw the flash and was almost immediately deafened by the report of the explosion. The next morning a large hole, fifty feet or more in diameter, was discovered in the ice about 600 feet from shore. The ice was solid in this spot the day before. For a long distance around the surface was cracked and broken and the ice around the hole itself, being twelve or fifteen inches in thickness, had the appearance of being driven down. The*

water at this spot is only eight or ten feet deep and the bottom of the lake is soft and muddy.

Carp Lake is an early name for Lake Leelanau; Fouch's dock is at the extreme southern end. The community of Fouch, consisting of a few cabins and cottages, can be found on the oldest plat maps of the area. Clearly, a meteorite, perhaps more than one, lies in shallow water in the lake—and we know approximately where it is. Not only that, with a hole in the ice approximately fifty feet in diameter, we can make guesses about how big it is.

Russia, in 2013 also struck the frozen surface of a lake. It left a hole about 23-26 feet in diameter, from which a five-foot long meteorite was pulled some time after the event occurred. If the Lake Leelanau meteorite left a hole twice as big, it may have an even larger fragment–though such size estimations are difficult to predict, since it is possible—even likely—that the fragment broke up into smaller pieces upon impact.

Would modern imaging techniques reveal the under-lake location of the 1879 meteorite? Even if located, could such an object be easily brought to the surface? The Chelyabinsk meteorite weighed 1250 pounds before it broke apart into three pieces. How much more would an object that produced a fifty-foot hole in the ice weigh? We do not know the answers to these questions—but wouldn't it be fun to find out?

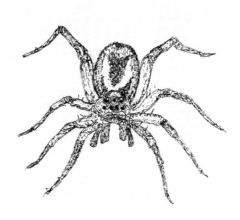

FOR THE LOVE OF SPIDERS

In winter the animal world goes to sleep—or, at least becomes less apparent to us. In particular, the world of small living things disappears, the world of insects, millipedes, centipedes—and spiders.

The absence of spiders is particularly distressing. They decorate my dwelling place inside and out during summer and fall. In my youth I have been known to keep them as erstwhile pets, feeding them a disabled fly, perhaps, or some other insect. Once, when I was in early adolescence, I kept a funnel-web weaver in my room, sustaining it with insect prey well into winter until my mother vacuumed it one day, not understanding my attachment to the animal. The haiku poet Issa says,

Don't worry, spiders,
 I keep house
casually.

We are of like mind.

I am hardly an expert in spiders: I encounter them separately as each enters my consciousness—by chance, not searching them out. Some, like the funnel-web weaver can be identified by the shape of its web, a sheet of silk that tapers to a narrow opening where its inhabitant lives. The orb weaver makes a gorgeous web with spokes and concentric circles. I love the name of one of them, Argiope aurantia, a name that comes from one of the Greek naiads or water spirits. She—and the inhabitants of webs are female—weaves a gorgeous structure out of the finest silk to capture whatever small thing blunders its way into the sticky strands, a story both horrifying and fascinating. I confess as a child tearing of a leg of a grasshopper and feeding the twitching body to a yellow-bodied Argiope aurantia, poised in her web to bite and wrap up her prey. Far from signaling the beginnings of major psychosis, it was just a small child's introduction to life-and-death, an encounter that stays with me still.

Wolf spiders terrify us with their size—with legs extended they barely fit in a teacup—their furry bodies, and their speed as they flee from us or go after prey. Similar to them are fishing spiders, one of which, the Dark Fishing Spider is the largest spider in North America, its body more than an inch long. It journeys far from water, often winding up in cabins and homes near the water. It feeds upon full grown crickets and small children (just joking). A naturalist friend of mine recently emailed me an image of one she caught in her home close to West Grand Traverse Bay. With compassion, she merely let it go outside her home rather than crushing it with her heel.

Then there are the jumping spiders, nervous creatures with two great eyes in the front of its head, looking more like us that all the others. They build no webs at all, preferring to wander about in search of prey, dragging a silk thread behind them. With so much to say about them, they deserve a separate article in the Grand Traverse Journal.

Finally, there are the cellar spiders, the most common ones we see around the house. With long legs and narrow bodies, they are sometimes erroneously called "daddy long legs spiders", a term that signifies the harvestmen, not a spider at all. They hang upside down in its poorly crafted web, a "cobweb" waiting for prey. My favorite spider book, Spiders of the North Woods, tells me that when disturbed, they may shake their bodies, making them appear as a blur. I will have to test that out.

Are spiders dangerous? Not for the most part. The Black Widow does have a poisonous bite and I have seen them around here. A bite would sicken the victim but not kill him/her. Other spiders hurt if they bite, but most of them cannot even penetrate the skin.

FOR THE LOVE OF SPIDERS

Many wounds attributed to spiders were caused by other vermin, fleas, ticks, or insects.

We need to show them respect, especially in the winter when we see few wild living things close to the house. Maybe we can let the cellar spiders live out the cold months—at least as long as they stay in the cellar

VENTIFACT FIELDS
WHERE WIND POLISHES AND ERODES

Some years ago I took a summer geology course from Central Michigan University at its Beaver Island Biological Station. The professor, an enthusiastic geologist named Richard Dietrich, introduced me to such wonders as vugs, banded gneiss, rhyolite porphyry, and ventifacts. While much of the knowledge gained about these topics has inexplicably evaporated into thin air, I do recall ventifacts in some detail, perhaps because I have identified several ventifact fields locally.

Students of Latin may know the meaning of "ventifact" from the word itself. It is derived from the word *ventus*, wind, from which we get "vent" and "ventilation". A ventifact is an object, often a stone, which has been shaped by the wind. A ventifact field, sometimes called a "lag gravel", is a place where such things are found—often in dry sandy places like a desert or the surface of the planet Mars.

Lag gravels are associated with sandy beaches liberally mixed with stones, but not every such beach is a lag gravel. The beach must be exposed to long fetch of prevailing winds, not protected by nearby bluffs or foredunes. It also should be protected from invasions of humans piloting vehicles at the shore or bearing beach paraphernalia: Frisbees, beach balls, volleyball nets, and all other such sources of amusement. Ventifacts are only found where human traffic is at a minimum.

How is a ventifact field different from an ordinary beach? The simplest way to tell is by looking at the stones in relation to the sand: Are they embedded or perched? Perched stones stand up on the surface, the surrounding sand having been blown away. The stones themselves, upon careful observation with a magnifier, display the characteristics of wind-driven abrasion: a high polish on exposed surfaces of those made of hard minerals like granite and a pitted, eroded surface on those composed of softer rock.

Polished stones shine in the sunlight on surfaces exposed to the wind, the surface resting on the ground showing no such luster even if washed and dried. Fossils stand out in relief as the softer stone around them wore down: Petoskey stones are especially striking, not requiring the usual hand polishing required to bring out their design. Best of all (for me) are the sedimentary rocks like siltstone or shale which, under ten power magnification, look like miniature scenes from eroded places out west like the Badlands of North Dakota or rocky areas of New Mexico. Mixed in with the rocks are occasional pieces of weathered glass or slag from old iron smelting operations. They frequently find a place upon windowsills or within boxes people keep to remember their experiences. Artifacts like these connect us with those who lived here long ago.

How does the wind polish and erode ventifacts? At first it was thought that blowing sand did the job, but on closer inspection, it turned out that wind-driven dust (derived from sand) played the most important role. It takes a mighty wind to lift sand, but less to blow dust. Stones can be polished even on days of lighter winds.

I won't tell you exactly where ventifact fields are because I do not want to increase human traffic in these precious places, but I will tell you this: Sleeping Bear National Lakeshore has them. So does one isolated beach along Grand Traverse Bay. If you go out looking for one, remember to look for a broad beach with perched stones—and the stones do not have to be large—they can be only pebble-sized. Be sure to bring your magnifier, at least ten power. To see the fossils in relief, the shiny surfaces, and eroded landscapes you will need at least that magnification. If you find a ventifact field, be guarded as to whom you tell. There are places endangered for their geology as well as for their biology. We need to protect them, too.

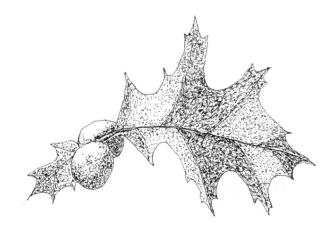

THE TRUTH ABOUT OAK APPLES

Oak apples are clearly a fraud. Everyone knows oaks make acorns, not apples. Still, the term exists—and if you look carefully in mid- to late summer, you might even find them. Oaks grow in Northern Michigan, occupying the northern boundary of their range with few individuals being found in the Upper Peninsula. In Traverse City we can find white oaks—those with rounded leaf lobes—and members of the red oak group—those with pointed lobes.

Compared to real apples, oak apples are puny, only a couple of inches in diameter, lacking both the texture and the crunch of the real thing. If you open the firm papery shell of one, you may find long, stringy fibers extending from the rind to a central nucleus. Alternatively, you may find that space filled with spongy matter like packing material. This wooly stuffing contains tannin, a brown pigment that especially suited for artwork and documents of many kinds. Here is a recipe typical of that Leonardo da Vinci might have used:

> *Take an ounce of beaten gaule, three or four ounces of gum arabicke, put them together in a pot of raine water, and when the gum is almost consumed, strain it through a cloath, and put into it almost halfe a cup of victriall beaten to a powder.* ~ A Booke of Secrets (1596) p. 5

Gum Arabic, a gum from the acacia tree, was used as a binder for the ink; "victriall" (vitriol) was nothing more than iron sulfate, obtained from passing water through "sulfurous earth" and exposing it to iron. The resulting ink has a bold blue-black appearance, though it fades to brown as manuscripts age. Many of the world's finest artists employed gall ink in their drawings, Rembrandt and Van Gogh to name two, and composers like Mozart regularly used it for their musical scores. The permanence of the ink is demonstrated by the masterpieces that remain for us to enjoy today.

If apples are fruit, then oak apples are not—since they do not contain seeds. That being the case, what causes oak apples to form? The answer lies with a tiny wasp, *Amphibolips confluens*.

In early summer the wasp deposits its egg on a young leaf. The egg and the larva that grows from it secrete plant growth substances that compel the oak to make the oak apple. After growing inside its comfortable chamber, the young wasp emerges to find a mate—both sexes are produced in equal numbers. After mating, the females crawl down the trunk to lay their eggs on the roots of the host oak tree. The young that hatch are all females produced by parthenogensis–no males involved! They spend the winter underground, feeding casually on the roots as needed, but mostly remaining dormant until the weather warms. When the young oak leaves are just the right size, they ascend the tree trunk to lay their eggs, thereby completing the life cycle.

Oak apples are not the only galls formed on oaks. In fall in Northern Michigan white oaks shower the ground with pea-sized leaf galls, each one carrying a larva wasp. Acorns and twigs harbor still more galls, all caused by the same family of wasps, the cypnids. It is hopeless to wipe them out, the two species, wasps and oaks, having evolved together for untold generations. Besides, who would want to? Galls are fascinating objects and useful, too. Won't you find a tree full of oak apples and make your own ink this summer?

HORSETAILS
RELIC PLANTS BEFORE THE DINOSAURS

We have all seen them, on the beach or in ditches, but we walk on past them without a thought. If we know them at all, we call them "snake grass" for their banded stems lacking apparent leaves. As kids, we pulled them apart at the joints, noting the empty, hollow canal that runs up the center. Hollow stems suggest many uses to children—whistles, building materials for sand castles, girls' hair ties, toothpicks, and more. Not having lost the capacity for play, they find much to do with the things we have come to ignore.

Not that all adults ignore them. Campers recognize one species as a choice pot scrubber out in the woods, the scouring rush, *Equisetum hyemale.* Its stiff ridged stems take grease and dirt of pans without shredding. Players of instruments like the bassoon and oboe prepare their reeds with strokes of the scouring rush and craftsmen in Japan use it for a fine sandpaper.

Snake grass, or horsetails as they are known by many, get their roughness and strength from silica in their stems—you can see the tubercles with a ten-power lens. Some species have more than others: one, the Smooth Horsetail, scarcely has any at all.

The Dutch find value in horsetails, mostly in maintaining the dikes that keep their land dry. The plant has deeply rooted rhizomes (horizontal underground stems) which bind the soil, a helpful aid in reinforcing walls that keep the sea out. A weed anywhere else, it is an asset in Holland.

The common name "horsetail" requires explanation since the above-ground parts of the plant in no way resembles any part of the horse's anatomy. If you have the patience to dig down into the mud out of which the horsetail species known as "pipes" grows (and, I confess, I did just that at some sacrifice of blood to mosquitoes), you can discover how they came to take on the "horsetail" name. The rhizome is jointed just like the stem, and out of each joint a tuft of roots grows—which, in aggregate, look pretty much like a horse's tail. Perhaps "snake grass" is the more reasonable name given the difficulty with exposing the "tail."

Horsetails are not particularly successful as green plants go: they consist of one family with one genus and only a scant 15 species. Michigan has eight and all of them be found in the Grand Traverse area. Always they seem to prefer wet places—ditches, beaches, swamps, and marshes.

Horsetails were not always the weak sisters of the plant world. Giant members of the horsetail family that reached heights of 45 feet are preserved in the coal beds of Pennsylvania and elsewhere. Before the dinosaurs, before the flowering plants, they dominated the land in variety, abundance, and sheer size. Alas for them, they now grow in neglected places separated from the great ecosystems of hard and softwood forests, plains and desert, tundra and bog.

Seed-producing plants won out in the long run, the conifers, hardwoods, and grasses occupying the greatest stretches of land. Horsetails make spores, those produced in small cones that lie at the tips of the shoots. They drift about in the wind, the luckiest ones arriving at a moist warm place to grow. There they grow into miniscule green bodies that produce eggs in one place and sperms in another. The sperms swim to fertilize the egg—and a new horsetail is born. However, horsetails can avoid the whole process by having a piece of the rhizome break off and root elsewhere.

Horsetails—snake grass–are not esteemed by those who wish to keep their beaches well-groomed. Their roots are hard to tear out—remember the Dutch and their dikes?—causing them to reappear after great effort has been exerted to remove them. Still, we should appreciate their good qualities: they scour, they sandpaper, they can be tied. Not only that, they provide a glimpse into a different world 350 million years ago. If you see a millipede hanging out among the stems of horsetails, you might be looking out on a scene enacted 380 million years ago. Horsetails deserve our respect for their venerable age.

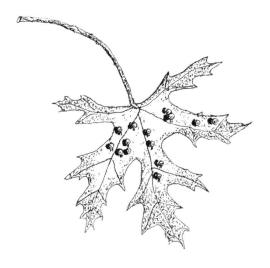

GROWING YOUR OWN HOUSE
THE MITES OF MAPLE BLADDER GALLS

In early summer you may have noticed small pouches on red and silver maple leaves. If you open one up, you will find—nothing at all. Or so it seems. In fact, the creatures that live there are swarming all around.

They are microscopic mites of the eriophyid family, so small you would need a 400X magnification to study them in detail. Unlike most mites, they have but four legs—not eight—with two pairs clustered around the animal's mouth. Dwelling within such a small space, eriophyids hardly have need of legs at all: for most of their lives their universe is no bigger than the gall they inhabit.

The life cycle of the mite is simple. They mate and reproduce within the secure enclosure of the gall, producing several generations within a summer. Before leaves change color in autumn, obeying a signal we do not know, they migrate out of their chamber to the bud scales of next year's leaves or to protected areas under loose bark. Dormant, they wait there for the cold blast of winter.

In spring, before leaves expand, they enter young leaves on the underside, their presence initiating the balloon-growth of many pouches, the number ranging from a half dozen or so to an ugly multitude that deforms the leaf. While the mites undoubtedly sap energy from trees, they cause little permanent damage. Gardeners and foresters generally ignore their presence, not wasting effort or chemicals to discourage them.

I think leaves adorned with crimson maple bladder galls are attractive, resembling miniature Christmas decorations in the month farthest removed from that holiday. They can be pointed or inflated depending upon the species of mite involved and colors vary, frequently starting off green and becoming red before fading to a dull brown. Can they be thought of as a rash trees get? Not exactly, since they do infect the surface tissues alone, unlike human dermatitis.

Another kind of eriophyid attacks plants in a different way. Instead of making galls, it secretes a chemical that induces plants to grow a forest of slender hairs called an erineum. An erineum—taken from the Greek word for fleece—can be found on the lower surface of leaves of many plants: oaks, maples, viburnum, and grapes are especially affected. It may appear as a velvet fuzz, white or commonly red in color.

As with the gall-forming eriophyids, the erineum mites are exceedingly difficult to see even with a powerful magnifier.

A twenty-power lens might reveal their presence, though sharp eyes will be called for. A microscope, of course, would work better.

Somehow I connect these animals with larger herbivores like bison.. I imagine them roaming over the fields of hairs they caused to grow, feeding upon them as the bison would, a prairie in a square inch. Throughout early summer they graze, finally retiring to bud scales and bark for the winter. Occasionally a stiff wind will blow them right out of the erineum, something bison do not have to worry about. Of course, the advantage for the mite is that it might get blown to a new tree, fertile ground to establish a new miniature prairie ecosystem.

Nature performs its work at every scale: planet, ecosystem, organism, organs, tissues, and cells. Isaac Asimov, the famous science fiction writer, once wrote about exploring the world extending from his backdoor. After much study he had gotten as far as a few feet from his porch, so numerous were the species he encountered. Most likely he did not get around to the mite-formed galls or erineums on his shade trees.

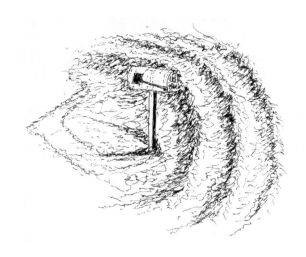

SUDDEN FLOODING ALONG THE BAY
ARE WE DUE FOR ANOTHER SEICHE?

How many times has it happened? Along East Bay, usually at night or early morning, the water surges up, rising four feet or more from its normal level, only to subside within minutes. In the past, roads have been flooded, docks floated away, and debris swept into the water. Houses and cottages have been flooded and cars damaged by the flooding such that they had to be towed away for repair. West Bay gets them, too, but East Bay, especially at the south end, from Five Mile road west to the Birchwood area of Traverse City have been especially hard-hit.

The 1950's experienced a number of these events, not just locally, but throughout all the Great Lakes. At first, no one knew what to make of them: newspapers called them "Tidal Waves," often using quotation marks since everyone knew they had nothing to do with the tides. The only similarity is that the water rose somewhat gradually, and not with an abrupt crash of giant waves on the shore. In 1952, the *Traverse City Record Eagle* declared no one knew what caused them, but that observation was soon to change: a surge of water with immense waves swept up on the Chicago shore on June 26, 1954, causing the deaths of ten persons. That tragedy sparked interest among scientists studying the phenomenon. They would soon uncover the causes.

Gordon E. Dunn, Meteorologist-in-charge of the Chicago office, realized that, on past occasions, the surges always occurred after the arrival of a pressure increase associated with a rapidly moving storm front coming from the north. On July 6, 1954, just ten days after the devastating surge described above, conditions looked nearly identical to those of that day. Based upon his understanding of the event, Dunn issued the first seiche warning. Somewhat to his surprise given his scant knowledge, a moderate seiche did strike Chicago, one that caused little damage, much to the relief of all.

Since those early times, we have learned much more about seiches. They are associated with fast-moving storm lines, especially those moving faster than 50km/hr. There must be a significant pressure rise associated with those lines, with a long fetch of water covering the entire width of a body of water—Lake Michigan or Grand Traverse Bay—making for more the most dramatic events. One factor Dunn did not understand was the most fundamental thing of all: storm surges bounce off shores and send reflected waves outward to interact with those coming in. It is like a basin of water with a water disturbance that reflects off the sides, sometimes building into surges that are magnified by the coming together of different waves. Surges and the receding of water can go on for days as waves interact, just as water in a basin takes time to settle if it is disturbed. All of this happens during seiches.

East Bay presents another aspect of seiches. It has vast shoals— shallow areas—that extend from the south and west shores. When rising water strikes them, waves grow taller, driving farther inland. One of the descriptions of a seiche claims that the water rushed 30 to 40 feet inland from its usual position, but only in areas at the base of the Bay. This "shoaling" effect is known to increase the severity of seiches.

East Bay also presents an obstructed range of open water (a "fetch") that enables waves free travel down its length. By contrast, West Bay has a narrowing at Lee's Point on the west side and Bower's Harbor on the east, after which it widens at the south end. Contours of the land also affect the severity of seiches, and East Bay seems especially suited to maximize high water surges.

This is not to say West Bay has not experienced them. On April 1, 1946, a resident of Bay Street in Traverse City reported the water level rose two feet before subsiding. An older story is told that in March, 1891, the city had been withdrawing water from West Bay for household use by means of an intake pipe that extended two hundred feet from the shore under twenty feet of water. When the pumps started racing one morning, it was realized that no water was being moved at all. Upon breaking the ice that covered the intake, it was discovered that the water had receded to the point that the mouth of the pipe wasn't in the water at all. Soon after, water levels rose, and residents were able to get water for their morning coffee. The peculiarity of this event—occurring when the Bay was frozen—sets one to wondering if some factor besides a seiche wasn't operating.

East Bay experienced three significant seiches in the two years 1952-53. The May 5, 1952 seiche is interesting because we have access to hour-by-hour data about wind speed and direction. Hour-by-hour after midnight the wind direction changed: 1:00 AM: out of the East at 7 mph; 2:00 AM: out of the west at 7 mph; 3:00 AM: out of the south at 10 mph: 4:00 AM: out of the west at 8 mph; 5:00 AM: out of the north at 12 mph. The wind direction stayed out of the north after that time for the rest of the day. Note the time of day: after midnight and early morning. For reasons not completely understood, the biggest surges of water tend to happen in early morning up to noon. Also note that the wind direction jumps from one direction to another, finally ending with a strong wind out of the north. The effect is to pile up water on one side of the Bay, only to have it rush in from the north. Given the contours of that body of water, that is exactly what you would expect in order for the biggest surge of water to occur at the southern end.

Residents on the south shore of East Bay notified the sheriff of the flooding shortly after 4:00 AM, a time fairly consistent with the wind change out of the north. After the first surge, water rose again and again, but never reached the high water mark of the first rush. That behavior goes along with our present understanding of seiches as disturbances in a closed basin with waves that reinforce each other at times.

When will the next seiche be? Who can say? We should beware when a fast-moving storm line moves in from the north associated with rapidly rising air pressure. The National Weather Service now issues warnings when conditions are favorable for water surges and high waves, and persons living in vulnerable places should take precautions to protect their lives and property. It has been some time since the last big one and it is easy to become complacent in the absence of memory. After all, Nature acts whether we are ready or not for what she gives us.

GRAPE FERNS AND THE ART OF BECOMING INVISIBLE

In late spring, when the morel hunters and spring wildflower admirers have disappeared from the woods, I go out in search of grape ferns, the Botrychiums. They are not good to eat, they do not possess colorful leaves, and they lack flowers altogether. Still, they have their strong points: for one thing, reputedly they can make the collector invisible. So far, I have been unable to demonstrate their potency in this regard, but given the antiquity of the claim, I will check it out one more time—the herbalists of old can't have been totally wrong on this one—or can they?

The Botrychiums (Greek for "grape") stand no more than a few inches high. Named for the cluster of spore-producing bodies (sporangia), they remind us of bunches of tiny grapes held above a single green leaf. I have always found the most common species, *Botrychium matricariodes*, among young maple saplings on bare ground swept clear of last year's leaves. As with morel hunting, you go along without seeing them for a time—and then, suddenly, you see the first and then another and another. They occupy a large area: dozens can be found at one place.

Botrychiums mostly spend their lives underground. First, spores must land at in an appropriate habitat. Upon arriving there, they grow underground, feeding upon nutrients produced by other plants by taking advantage of soil fungi that interconnect with their roots. After several years of growth–providing the above ground vegetation has progressed from weeds to young trees–grape ferns first appear above ground, finally shedding their spores to the wind. Thereafter, they sporadically appear every year—usually in late May and June—with some years better than others. After as long as 50 years, the habitat becomes unsuitable for them as trees age and the leaf litter becomes too thick for them to emerge above ground. They are not found in mature hardwoods.

Besides "grape ferns", Botrychiums are called "moonworts", after a species that produced leaflets reminiscent of half moons. This species alone confers invisibility to its bearer. In order for the spell to work, "fern seeds" must be gathered at midnight on June 23rd, St. John's Eve, the shortest night of the year. Here we must pause: What are "fern seeds"? Hundreds of years ago people thought all green plants produced seed and were puzzled by the apparent absence of seeds in ferns. According to the ancient "doctrine of signatures," characters demonstrated by plants pointed to their use in medicine. If the seeds were invisible, then invisibility might be transferred to humans by the presence of the plant. (Of course, everything is wrong with this idea: the doctrine of signatures has no validity and ferns reproduce by nearly invisible spores, not seeds.)

In order to catch invisible fern seed a seeker needed to stack twelve pewter plates, placing the fern frond on the top one. The invisible seeds would drop through the stack, finally resting at the bottom-most plate. Of course, there were other necessary behaviors: he must go bare-footed, wear a shirt, and be in a religious state of mind. Even observing all of these conditions, he might suffer failure if wandering fairies steal the fern seed.

It is clear why my efforts to attain invisibility will likely fail: no pewter plates, no desire to walk barefoot through the woods, and the ever-present possibility of thievish fairies. In fact, no fern seed at all. Most likely moonworts will not unshoe horses that step on them, loosen iron nails, or break chains by their touch. Nor will they empower woodpeckers to peck holes through iron if rubbed upon their beaks (a feat rather difficult to accomplish!). No, grape ferns only bring joy to their discoverers in the month of June. They bestow no particular virtues—no invisibility, no uncanny ability to penetrate iron. Still, they please us by their mere presence—much as the returning songbirds do. Look for them in June on bare hillsides wherever young trees grow.

OTHER BOOKS BY RICHARD FIDLER

In some places history lurks just under the surface. An old factory whispers a story about its workers a hundred years ago. An ancient oak with its trunk curiously bent suggests times before white settlement. GATEWAYS TO GRAND TRAVERSE PAST identifies these magical places and tells the stories connected with them.

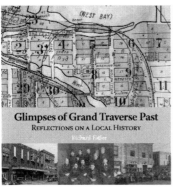

In discussions focused on important historical events, artifacts, and institutions of the Grand Traverse area, GLIMPSES OF GRAND TRAVERSE PAST explores who we are and how we got that way. Illustrated with archived photographs, it presents a refreshingly new perspective on Grand Traverse history.

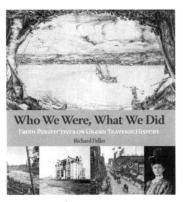

- *A hundred years ago, who were the poor in Grand Traverse County and how were they taken care of?*
- *How did human interventions change Grand Traverse Bay since white settlement?*

WHO WE WERE, WHAT WE DID answers these and other questions in short, lively discussions of social, political, environmental, and moral issues. This is a book for all who love this beautiful region of Michigan and wish to learn more about it.

TRAVERSE CITY, MICHIGAN
A Historical Narrative, 1850-2013
RICHARD FIDLER

One hundred-sixty-five years ago the Boardman River emptied its waters into the West Arm of Grand Traverse Bay amid a vast forest of white pines, red pines, and oak trees. But for occasional villages of Odawa Indians, the area was largely uninhabited. Sixty years later, the forests had disappeared, replaced by factories, an Asylum, schools, and churches as a primitive settlement grew into a small town. In time, the community shrank as residents moved away in search of better lives. Still, change was not done: people began to return, seeking the grace the land and water offered them as they reinvented the basis upon which their lives were built. This is the story of Traverse City, Michigan and it is the story of this book.

Illustrated with historic photographs and aerial views of Traverse City.

———————————————————————

RICHARD FIDLER has been a student and teacher of biology for more than fifty years. He is a graduate of the University of Michigan, B.A (Biology), M.S. (Biology), and Ed.D. (Science Education), and went on to teach secondary school biology for thirty-one years. Fascinated by the history of the Grand Traverse area, he has written four books on that subject. This is his first about the natural history of that area.

Made in the USA
Las Vegas, NV
30 July 2022